ROCK SOLID
The Geology of Nuclear Waste Disposal

Elspeth Reid obtained an M.A. in English and French Literature from Edinburgh University. After periods working in Spain, Malawi and Tanzania, she obtained an Open University Science Degree, specialising in Earth Sciences, and then an M.Sc from Aberdeen University. At present she is a Lecturer at Inverness College, and a Tutor with the Open University.

ROCK SOLID
The Geology of Nuclear Waste Disposal

Elspeth Reid

THE TARRAGON PRESS
Glasgow

ISBN 1 870781 03 1

A CIP catalogue record for this book is available from the
British Library.

Cover design and illustrations by Edward MacMillan

Typeset by Venture Computer Typesetting
Printed by Gilmour and Lawrence, Glasgow

For Brendan and Anna

CONTENTS

ACKNOWLEDGEMENTS

Many friends, colleagues and teachers have contributed to my understanding of the diverse earth sciences touched on in this book. I am grateful to them all, for no book can honestly be labelled 'all my own work'.

In particular I would like to thank Jane Clarke for her perceptive and helpful comments on an earlier draft; Geoff Yarwood for his practiced and sympathetic grafting and hedge-trimming; and last but not least, David Sumner, without whose invariably good advice and sometimes subtle encouragement this book might never have been completed.

FIGURE ACKNOWLEDGEMENTS

Grateful acknowledgement is made to the following for permission to reproduce diagrams in this book:

United Kingdom Nirex Ltd., for:

Figures 2.5 and 9.6   Predicted cross-section of the geology at Sellafield (simplified)

Figure 9.4   Predicted cross-section of the geology at Dounreay (simplified)

Figure 9.1   Possible repository sites

Figures 1.2 and Figure 9.2, both from Nirex Report No. 71 (1989)

UK Atomic Energy Authority for Figures 6.1 and 7.1 (both from Nirex Report NSS/G108)

The British Geological Survey for Figure 8.1, taken from *Seismol. Bull. Inst. Geol. Sci.*, No. 4, 1976, by R C Lilwall
Crown Copyright 1976

PREFACE

Discussion of social, political, economic and moral issues flour-
ishes wherever the topic of radioactive waste disposal is raised.
Everyone has their penny or pound to contribute. Equally, almost
everyone accepts – or possibly ignores – the claim that it is geology
which is at the heart of the safety argument for underground
disposal of nuclear wastes; that it is the rocks which would act
as the main safety barrier, protecting us and future generations
from radiation.

Why this acceptance? The answer isn't hard to find. Precious few
members of the public are scientists; few scientists are geologists;
and only a handful of geologists find the time to communicate
their knowledge and enthusiasm for the subject to the general
public. Volcanoes and earthquakes are all very well in the papers
or on television (they are disasters after all, not science) but fluid
flow in the subsurface, or the joys of clay minerals, don't on the
face of it, seem very exciting.

Walk into any decent bookshop and look for a science section.
You will find biology, chemistry, medical science, physics and
even geography books displayed in convincing numbers. But
where is geology? As likely or not, it is somewhere in a no-man's
land between astronomy and mountaineering. With a few hon-
ourable exceptions, geology scarcely figures in our school educa-
tion system and the popular consciousness. No wonder otherwise
independently-minded people, who would argue the hindleg off a
politician, economist or moralist, are reduced to cheerfully and
uncritically accepting whatever they are told about the safety of
underground nuclear waste disposal.

This book has been written in the conviction that the subject is
fascinating, topical, and at least as accessible to those of a
curious turn of mind as many other specialist fields of study. I
hope it is also useful, since some understanding of what geological disposal and geological containment of nuclear waste really

mean is a prerequisite for a sensible debate and democratic decision-making.

With a number of nuclear submarines and power stations due to be closed down in the next decade, the stores of radioactive waste, as well as the arguments about whose back yard it should end up in, will be hotting up. Whatever the direction taken by the nuclear industry in Britain, the legacy of waste is with us for the forseeable future, and decisions about its fate are being taken by 'experts', by politicians and by commercial companies offering technological fixes. The rest of us, who fall into none of these categories, may wish to ask about their plans and to understand what is being proposed and enacted in our names.

This book, I hope, will help us to see the way forward.

Elspeth Reid

Inverness
November 1989

Chapter 1

Nuclear Waste — What's the Problem?

'...there's no doubt that people are petrified at the thought of nuclear waste dumps on their doorsteps...'

Melanie Phillips, *The Guardian*, October 1989

'Britain's nuclear power industry continues to struggle in its efforts to gain public acceptance for a waste disposal strategy...'

Simon Hadlington, *Nature*, 2 June 1988

'People seem to fear nuclear waste dumps even more than nuclear power facilities.'

Stan Openshaw, Steve Carver, John Fernie

Britain's Nuclear Waste: Siting and Safety, 1989

This book is concerned with the disposal of radioactive waste materials produced by all the industrial activities which use radioactive substances. It is estimated that about 2 million tonnes of nuclear waste will have to be disposed of by the year 2030.

Our modern industrial society produces vast quantities of waste of all kinds. Household refuse alone in England and Wales amounts to 30 million tonnes a year — that's about half a ton for every man, woman and child. On top of this, coal mining produces 50 million tonnes of waste per year, and there are 10 million tonnes of other hazardous industrial wastes. In comparison, a total of two million tonnes of radioactive waste over the next forty years does not seem a great deal. So why all the fuss about radioactive waste (or nuclear waste as it is usually called)? There are some who argue that, amongst all the many types of toxic industrial waste, nuclear waste receives more than its fair share of attention and concern. Nevertheless there is no doubt that radioactive substances, especially if taken into the body, can be hazardous; so nuclear waste does need to be stored, or disposed of, in such a way that the exposure of the public to radioactive substances is as low as possible.

The problem is particularly difficult to solve for the following reasons.

1. Radioactivity in materials cannot be destroyed by any physical means (such as boiling, baking or burning), nor by any chemical means (adding chemicals of any sort).

2. There is some natural radioactivity in the environment, and indeed in some areas, natural radioactivity reaches levels greater than those permitted in industrial uses of radioactivity. Any radioactivity released into the environment by industrial uses is, however, added to the natural levels already present.

3. Exposure to *high* levels of radioactivity undoubtedly results in an increased risk of cancer. However, the size of the cancer risk resulting from exposure to *low* levels of radioactivity is much less certain, and indeed controversial. It is generally assumed that any exposure to radioactivity (natural or artificial) carries some extra (albeit small) risk of cancer.

4. Radioactive materials *do* become less radioactive as time passes. For some materials, the radioactivity drops to very low levels after days or hours. For many others, however, it takes years, thousands of years, or even millions of years.

Radioactive waste materials therefore have the potential to produce adverse effects on living systems for many generations into the future. It may therefore be prudent to ensure that any additions to natural levels of radioactivity are avoided, or at the very least minimised.

A discussion of what radioactivity actually is, and of how the use of nuclear reactors for the generation of electricity leads to the production of radioactive waste, is in Appendix 1.

Types and quantities of waste

Radioactive waste in Britain is divided into three categories, low level waste (LLW), intermediate level waste (ILW) and high level waste (HLW). Typically, HLW is a thousand times more radioactive than ILW, which in turn is typically a thousand times more radioactive than LLW; it will take hundreds of thousands, or even hundreds of millions of years, for HLW to decay to LLW. It is also important to note that the divisions between the three categories of waste are rather arbitrary; some ILW will be not very different from some HLW, while some ILW will be more like LLW.

High level waste consists mainly of spent fuel rods from the cores of nuclear power stations, and waste products from reprocessing. It is literally too hot to handle — the high levels of radioactivity generate large amounts of heat. This kind of waste will probably need to be stored for around fifty years to allow some of the heat to disperse, before it can be processed for disposal.

HLW from reprocessing is currently stored at Sellafield and Dounreay as a concentrated liquid. The best way of dealing with it is thought to be vitrification, which literally means turning it into glass. In fact the waste would be mixed with natural minerals and turned into a very fine-grained imitation rock called Synroc, designed to be both chemically and physically stable for long periods of time. The vitrified product will be stored in stainless steel containers, which will be air cooled. They will remain in storage for at least 50 years, after which the lower temperatures will make disposal easier.

Intermediate level waste comes mainly from the nuclear power industry and includes reactor components, fuel cladding, sludges, resins and filters. Some ILW also comes from hospitals and industry in the form of old radioactive sources for cancer therapy and industrial radiography.

Low level waste consists mainly of items such as protective clothing and laboratory equipment which may have come into contact with radioactive material.

A rule of thumb comparison of the relative volumes of the different levels of waste sometimes quoted by the nuclear industry is that for every teaspoonful of HLW there is a cupful of ILW and a pint of LLW. At present LLW is buried in trenches at the Drigg disposal site in West Cumbria, about six kilometres along the coast to the southeast of BNFL Sellafield.

The vast majority of ILW and HLW comes from nuclear fuel reprocessing at Sellafield, which increases the amount of waste by a factor of about 200 compared with the spent fuel rods. 4 cubic metres of spent fuel when reprocessed will produce: 2.5 cubic metres of HLW, 40 of ILW and 600 of LLW.

In future there will be a further source of nuclear waste which we have not yet mentioned — waste from decommissioning (closing down) old nuclear power stations and disposal of old nuclear submarines. This decommissioning process may need to be started soon, since the first nuclear power station has now been taken out of service, as has a nuclear submarine.

Estimates of the amounts of LLW and ILW which need to be dealt with in the next few decades have increased year by year. In 1987 the best available estimate was one and three quarter million

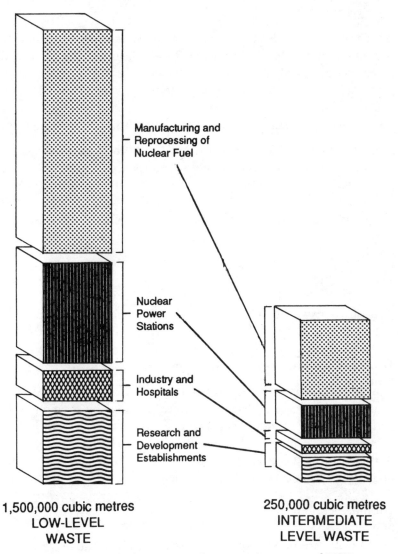

1,500,000 cubic metres
LOW-LEVEL
WASTE

250,000 cubic metres
INTERMEDIATE
LEVEL WASTE

Figure 1.1 Approximate volumes and sources of LLW
and ILW to be disposed of by Nirex. Military waste could
add 20% to the total. Estimates of the amount of civil
waste have increased annually.

cubic metres. In 1988 the House of Commons Radioactive Waste Management Advisory Committee (RWMAC) stated that predicted wastes arising up to the year 2030 were now 4% higher than previously estimated, as a result of including wastes from decommissioned power stations. RWMAC's estimate for total nuclear waste up to the year 2030 was nearly two million cubic metres.

By 1989, the figure for fifty years' accumulation had grown again to over two and a half million cubic metres (Nirex, 1989). Since it was subsequently announced in July 1989 that Britain's 9 oldest nuclear reactors would all be closed down by the year 2002, further upward revisions of the amount of waste to be disposed of may be necessary.

But what does two and a half million cubic metres of anything look like? Imagine an Olympic 100m relay team running round each of the four sides of a square instead of round a track, then mentally excavate to a depth of 250 metres (for comparison, the Eiffel Tower is about 300 m high), and then transport all the earth and rock away — you'll have about two and a half million cubic metres of soil and rock to dispose of.

In a deep radioactive waste repository, all the waste would have to be packed in steel drums and surrounded by concrete. In addition, plenty of room would be needed for access, ventilation, vehicles, equipment and workers. So a series of tunnels and caverns with a very much bigger volume than two and a half million cubic metres would be needed.

In 1987 attention in Britain was switched from HLW to the disposal of LLW and ILW. The decision was made for two reasons:

1. HLW cannot be disposed of immediately because of its high temperature.

2. It exists in relatively small volumes compared to ILW and LLW.

So in the late 1980's the British government's solution to the problem of radioactive waste disposal is as follows:

- set aside the problem of disposal of high level waste for the moment (but see Appendix 2)

- store all intermediate and low level waste in a single, national, underground repository.

Responsibility for disposal of ILW and LLW lies with a company called United Kingdom Nirex Ltd. which we shall refer to as Nirex. This stands for Nuclear Industry Radioactive Waste Executive. Nirex was originally set up in 1982 (with Government agreement) by British Nuclear Fuels plc, the South of Scotland Electricity Generating Board, the Central Electricity Generating Board and the United Kingdom Atomic Energy Authority. The Government, in the person of the Secretary of State for Energy, also holds a special share in Nirex. British Nuclear Fuels Ltd. undertake production of fuel rods for nuclear reactors, and also operate the reprocessing plant at Sellafield for recovery of uranium and plutonium from used fuel rods. The Electricity Generating Boards own and run nuclear power stations (as well as fossil fuel-burning power stations). The United Kingdom Atomic Energy Authority was originally constituted to design, fabricate and test nuclear weapons, but was subsequently given responsibility for research and design work for nuclear power stations.

Since 1987 Nirex Ltd has been charged with choosing sites for investigation, building a repository, and thereafter storing and managing the waste. At present, Nirex has been given no brief to manage HLW, and at the time of writing (December 1989) no policy statements have been made about the future management of HLW.

In March 1989, two sites — Sellafield in Cumbria and the experimental fast breeder reactor site at Dounreay on the north coast of Caithness — were announced as suitable for intensive investigation as potential repositories. Both were existing nuclear installations, chosen from a secret list of 12 possible sites and a short list of four.

Because of the controversy surrounding the issue, the names of the other possible sites were treated as confidential, but were said by Nirex to lie within the broadly defined areas of potentially suitable geology described in their consultation document *The Way Forward* in 1988 (Figure 1.2). However, Nirex Report 71 (Nirex, 1989), published after the announcement of the choice of Dounreay and Sellafield, showed revised areas of interest (Figure 9.2).

The time-scale announced by Nirex for developing a repository was as follows:

1989–91	Exploratory geological investigations
1991	Choice of one site and planning application
1991–1994	Public enquiry followed by planning consent
1996	Begin construction of repository
2005–2055	Repository operational with further construction continuing.

However, the RWMAC 1988 Report commented that there is 'enormous uncertainty whether a deep disposal site will be found, assessed and in place by 2005 as planned.'

Nirex's preliminary estimate is that about 14 million cubic metres of spoil (crushed rock) would need to be excavated to construct a repository. To put this in perspective, it is more than double the volume of spoil from the construction of the Channel Tunnel, making the repository by far the largest civil engineering project ever attempted in this country. The Nature Conservancy Council

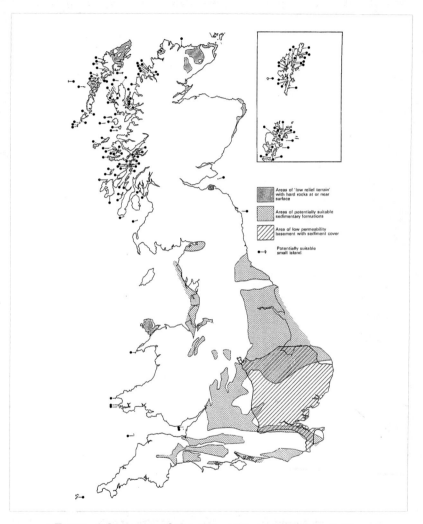

Figure 1.2 Areas of the UK with potentially suitable geology for a deep radioactive waste repository.

has noted that disposal of the spoil alone would present a formidable problem. [*Earth Science Conservation* No. 25, Dec 1988, Nature Conservancy Council]

The budget for the work is between sixteen thousand million and forty thousand million pounds sterling at 1989 prices. The wide range of anticipated costs may be to allow investigation of more than two sites, or to cater for larger volumes of waste.

Arguments

This is no chicken-hearted attempt to solve the problem of what to do with radioactive waste; it's big, it's expensive, it's radical. But why is it necessary to make such a radical change in the way we manage radioactive waste?

At present, the bulk of Britain's radioactive waste is buried in shallow trenches at the LLW disposal site at Drigg in Cumbria, which is owned by British Nuclear Fuels plc (BNFL). In 1988, the Radioactive Waste Management Advisory Committee warned that the tip would be full by the end of the century. However, figures provided by BNFL in 1989 have convinced the government that Drigg will not run out of space until 2020.

HLW and ILW are mainly stored above ground at the site where they are produced, which means mostly nuclear power stations and military establishments. In the summer of 1989, the ILW store of the experimental fast breeder reactor at Dounreay was even added to the tourist circuit of the establishment. Sellafield has also been successfully promoted as one of England's busiest tourist attractions. So why can't the present arrangements just continue?

Some of the arguments in favour of an underground repository are:

- The site at Drigg will be full in a few years and is not

satisfactory anyway.

- Deep underground burial will isolate the waste safely.

- Increasing volumes of waste resulting from reprocessing and decommissioning power stations can't be stored on site indefinitely.

- It's safer to have a single, properly monitored site than lots of smaller ones scattered about the country.

Arguments against are:

- deep disposal isn't the only option and we simply don't know enough to say if it is the best one.

- deeply buried waste would be difficult to monitor and impossible to retrieve if something went badly wrong.

- 'out of sight' could mean 'out of mind' and make people dangerously complacent about safety.

- we can maintain present arrangements for long enough to investigate solutions to the problem more comprehensively.

Geological Containment of Radioactive Waste

The idea behind deep disposal is that waste can be isolated, retained or contained several hundred metres below the ground surface for very long periods of time. The idea is that the rock surrounding an underground repository will act as a giant container for the waste and prevent it from getting back to the surface. This concept is often referred to as **geological containment of radioactive waste**; an underground repository can only be safe if geological containment is shown to operate effectively.

It is useful, when discussing containment and safety, to use the terms geosphere and biosphere. The **geosphere** is the underground world of rocks, and the **biosphere** is the surface world which supports life and consists of the air, soils, fresh and salt water and the plants and animals which inhabit them. At first sight biosphere and geosphere may seem quite separate, but there are many links between them. Some links consist of shared features such as water, gases and microbes. Another kind of link is in the physical and chemical processes which operate across the boundaries between the two worlds. The debate about how and whether containment will work is a debate about these links, for there is no dispute that geology is at the heart of the safety case for mined underground radioactive waste repositories.

Many different kinds of geologist can contribute to the pool of knowledge about the underground behaviour of radionuclides. Hydrogeologists specialise in studying the movement of water through rocks, geophysicists use measurements of minute changes in rock magnetism and mass,as well as artificially-generated ground vibrations, to produce astonishingly detailed interpretations of rock structures hundreds of metres below the surface; geochemists find out about the ways in which groundwater reacts with the surrounding rock — they can even estimate how old water is and where it has come from; geomicrobiologists study the micro-organisms which can flourish in apparently hostile, rocky environments. Mining geologists are familiar with a whole range of processes which affect or arise from humanity's determination to extract useful minerals from the earth's crust; and engineering geologists bridge the gap between constructions and their natural environment.

In all these diverse fields of work which come under the broad heading of 'geology', there are two common elements of concern — rock and water. In a deep repository, the rock would act as a containment vessel, but the water would be the principal problem because it can transport radionuclides back to the biosphere.

The basic ingredients in a recipe for geological containment are sometimes simply summarised as rock, water and radioactive wastes. And the recipe instructions? Mix the wastes with a lot of rock using as little water as possible. Cover tightly and leave undisturbed for a very long time.

It all seems quite straightforward until you start wondering what exactly all the different types of geologist listed above have been, and continue to be, so busy investigating. Doesn't that mean that what goes on in the geosphere must be a lot more complicated than the simple recipe indicates? The answer of course is — yes. It is quite easy to think of questions which need to be answered before anyone could judge whether the containment recipe would produce the desired results. For instance:

- What kind of rock?

- How much water is there and how fast does it move?

- Will radionuclides go wherever water does?

- What about gas?

- Where would various radionuclides end up if they did escape?

- What processes would make containment more effective?

- What processes would help radionuclides reach the bio-sphere?

- How can we be sure what will happen a long time in the future?

Unless such questions can be answered, following the simple recipe for deep disposal of radioactive wastes could produce some very unpredictable results. It would be a bit like not knowing whether the end product of your recipe would be carrot cake or lasagne; both are edible, both are baked, both contain vegetables, flour, oil and water — but there the resemblance ends. And the end product of the unpredictable containment recipe would be considerably less palatable!

There are however some good reasons for considering the option of geological containment. Chief among these are the restricted links between geosphere and biosphere (burying things underground for safekeeping is hardly a new idea) and the long time scale which applies to some geological processes. Fifty years is more than half a person's life, but geologists commonly talk in terms of millions of years. This is important in view of the fact that some radioactive waste can remain harmful to life for a very long time (see Appendix 1). Assessing safety and risks is not straightforward and is the subject of continuing research. All aspects of the geology must be thoroughly understood and we need to know exactly how, when and in what quantities radioactive substances could reach the biosphere. No-one expects engineered barriers of steel and concrete to last as long as the danger posed by the waste. This means that leakages from a repository will occur,and that what happens in the surrounding rock will determine whether there is, or is not, radioactive contamination of the biosphere.

Summary

The work which Nirex is proposing is the concentration of Britain's low and intermediate level radioactive waste at a single underground site over a period of fifty years or more. Some of this waste could pose a hazard for tens of thousands of years.

The question addressed by this book is: will geological containment of radioactive waste actually work effectively, and continue to work as long as is necessary? In other words, is an underground repository going to be safe?

It is true that there are complex scientific arguments involved. It is also true that many more people could contribute to the arguments aired by proponents and opponents of deep disposal given a basic understanding of what geological containment actually involves. The Radioactive Waste Management Committee commented in its 1988 report that 'in many instances a sense of perspective of risk was lost when information was presented to the general public.' If this is true, it is a strong argument for making more information available; and if this book assists readers to ask appropriate questions and appreciate the implications of statements about geological containment of radioactive waste, it will have achieved its aim.

To understand the issues and arguments, a familiarity with some geological terms is necessary. So Chapter 2 begins to add some detail to the word 'geosphere' by briefly defining and illustrating some common rock types and their relationships.

Chapter 2

Rocks and Sediments

This Chapter is concerned with the names, dimensions and physical relationships of different types of rock and sediment. So it sets out, very briefly, to do five things:

1. Introduce some of the principal terms used to denote types of rock often referred to in public discussion of geological containment of radioactive waste.

2. Indicate the dimensions which are characteristic of some common types of rock.

3. Show the relationships between contrasting rock types in the geosphere.

4. Show how the rock of the geosphere may be blanketed with a variety of sediments and soils.

5. Point out the relationship between geological structures and landforms.

Rocks and minerals

First it is necessary to explain what we mean by a **mineral** and a **rock**. A **mineral** is a naturally occurring substance which has a definite crystalline structure. There are over two thousand different naturally occurring minerals, but the dominant rock-forming minerals fall into about half-a-dozen well-defined groups. Quartz is a common mineral and so are mica and pyrite (sometimes called fool's gold because of its gold-like appearance). A **rock** is just a mass or aggregate of mineral grains stuck together in some way. Usually the aggregate consists of a number of different kinds of minerals, but sometimes the grains may all be just one kind of mineral, such as halite (rock salt) or calcite (limestone).

There are three main groups of rocks: **igneous, metamorphic** and **sedimentary**. Some of the characteristic features of these groups are described below.

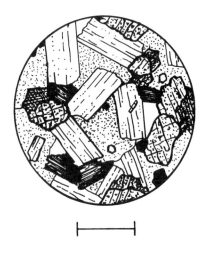

Figure 2.1 A crystalline rock seen through the micro-scope. The scale bar is 1 millimetre.

Most igneous and metamorphic rock is described as **crystalline**, implying that the rock is formed of a mass of interlocking mineral crystals (Figure 2.1). Crystalline rock is, generally speaking, relatively hard because of this tight interlocking of the crystals and thus is relatively resistant to physical change.

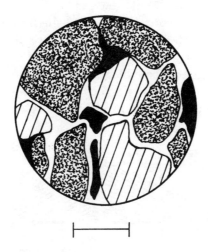

Figure 2.2 A sedimentary rock seen through the micro-
scope. Scale bar is 1 mm.

Most sedimentary rocks are fragmental (Figure 2.2), meaning that
the mineral grains were originally separate fragments, which are
now held together by a natural **cement** (nothing to do with
builders' cement except insofar as both stick things together).

Igneous and metamorphic rocks are often referred to collectively
as **hard rocks** while sedimentary rocks are called **soft rocks**. This
can be confusing, since a fourteen pound sledge hammer may
bounce off a well-cemented sedimentary rock with a ringing
sound, but break and crumble certain kinds of igneous rock.

Igneous rocks

These are rocks which have formed by cooling and solidification
of molten material (called **magma**) which has risen up from
deeper, and therefore hotter, layers of the Earth. Igneous rocks
are of two types.

The first includes **volcanic rocks** which were formed when molten **lava** and the products of various subterranean throat-clearings, such as clouds of ash, were suddenly ejected onto the surface of the Earth from volcanoes. As these lavas solidify into rocks, they form successive layers and through time build up in thick piles (Figure 2.3). An example of a volcanic rock is basalt.

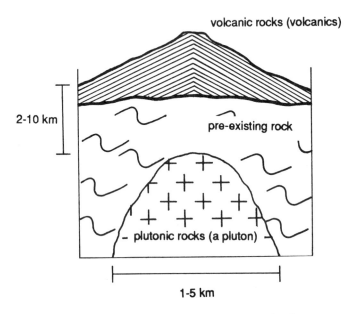

Figure 2.3 Igneous rocks — volcanic rocks forming a volcanic cone with layers sloping down away from the centre, overlying a plutonic intrusion at depth.

The other kind of igneous rocks form as massive bodies perhaps several kilometres below ground (Figure 2.3). They are known as **plutonic rocks** because they form below the Earth's surface, rising up in a molten state from deep in the realm of Pluto, the God of the Underworld of the Ancient Greeks. Plutonic igneous rocks can form fairly uniform masses, either domed like the one in the illustration, or sheet-like (much longer and wider than they are thick) in shape. Unlike layered volcanic rocks, they don't blanket the ground surface, but cut up through the pre-existing rocks. An example of plutonic rock is **granite**.

On a geological time-scale the surface of the Earth is constantly on the move, so volcanic rocks (volcanics for short), which started out at the surface many millions of years ago, may now be deeply buried. Similarly, granites which crystallised from molten rock (magma) two or three kilometres down, may now form hills at the surface.

Thinking of particular examples makes this clearer. For instance, the upper parts of some of the Cornish granites, which were formed at depth just under three hundred million years ago, are well-exposed at the surface today and form the familiar hills and tors. In the Cornish granites, kaolinite (china clay) has replaced other minerals. The granites have been brought to the surface by erosion and movements of the Earth's crust, and this allows open cast mining for china clay. The famous Red Hills of the Isle of Skye are also granites. Uplift of the Earth's crust, followed by erosion during past Ice Ages, has exposed the granites at the surface for us to admire (Figure 2.4). Other plutonic rocks remain hundreds of metres below the ground surface.

But what about the opposite case where rocks which started their life at or near the surface are now deeply buried beneath younger rocks of a quite different type? The geology of the coastal strip between Sellafield and the Cumbrian mountains provides a good example.

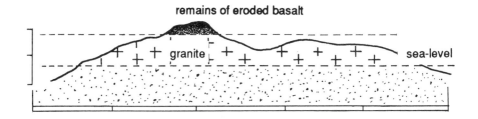

remains of eroded basalt

granite

sea-level

Figure 2.4 The Red Hills of Skye: Sheet-like bodies of granite now exposed at the surface.

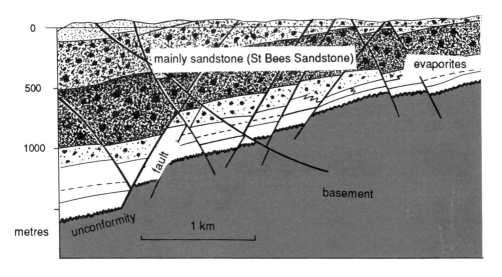

mainly sandstone (St Bees Sandstone)

evaporites

fault

basement

unconformity

1 km

Figure 2.5 Predicted cross-section through the upper part of the geosphere running NE from the Sellafield nuclear site.

Figure 2.5 shows a sketch cross-section running inland from the area of St. Bees Head, close to Sellafield. The rocks shown in the cross-section fall into two main divisions, sediments above and basement below. **Basement** simply means older rocks which have been deeply buried.

The basement rocks have the local name of **Borrowdale volcanics**. The word volcanics in Borrowdale volcanics indicates that when these rocks were formed they were at or near the Earth's surface. The vertical axis on the cross-section shows just how deeply the volcanics were later buried by sedimentary rocks — to a depth of over 900 metres at the coast. A few kilometres inland they lie only about 500 metres below the surface, and further inland still they are at the surface, forming the rugged hills of the Lake District.

Metamorphic rocks

Metamorphic rocks can form from any pre-existing rock. Movements of the Earth's crust result in rock formerly near the surface becoming deeply buried. Then heat and pressure acting over long periods of time cause alteration of the existing minerals of which the rock is composed, and the growth of new minerals. Since rock is defined as an aggregate of minerals, if the minerals change, the rock is changed into a different kind of rock. These changes are known to geologists as **metamorphism**.

Depending on the nature and extent of the metamorphic event, the resultant rock can be slightly or totally different from the original one. Like plutonic rocks, metamorphic rocks are formed from interlocking crystals which have grown together to form a tight, hard mass. The minerals usually show a distinct alignment reflecting the forces acting on the rock as they grew.

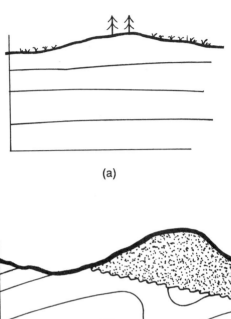

(a)

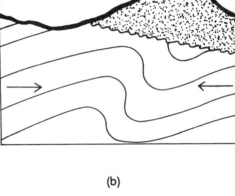

(b)

Figure 2.6 (a) Flat-lying sedimentary rocks.

(b) The rocks are deeply buried, heated and compressed so that they gradually fold. Minerals are transformed and the rocks are metamorphosed, and then uplifted and exposed at the surface by erosion.

Metamorphism affects zones of the geosphere extending laterally over tens or hundreds of square kilometres as well as to depths of many thousands of metres. Metamorphism is often accompanied by folding of the rocks (Figure 2.6). Small zones of metamorphic rock can also occur where the heat radiating from a plutonic rock has affected the **country rock** — a term for what was there before the plutonic rock (eg. a granite) forced its way in. Figure 2.3 shows metamorphosed country rock surrounding the pluton.

Common types of metamorphic rock are **schist** and **gneiss** (pronounced 'shist' and 'nice' respectively). Like all metamorphic rocks they are crystalline and form the surface and near-surface rocks of vast areas of the north and west of Scotland.

When veins of granite and associated rocks invade metamorphic country rock, the result can be a rock with a mixture of igneous and metamorphic components.

Sedimentary Rocks

Sediments consist of loose fragments (tiny or large) broken or worn off pre-existing rock. Sedimentary rocks are composed of accumulations of sediment which has been cemented together by naturally occurring minerals. For instance, **sandstone** is made from grains of sand held together usually by **calcium carbonate** or **quartz** cement (see Figure 2.2). Sometimes almost all the spaces between the sand grains are filled with cement and the rock is very hard. In other cases there are lots of spaces between the particles through which water (or oil or gas) can move. When there are lots of spaces the rock can be more easily broken up.

Some sedimentary rocks are formed largely from particles too tiny to see even with a microscope. These are known as **mudrocks**, or as **shales** if they split up easily into thin layers. These rocks are composed mainly of **clay minerals** cemented together.

Not all deposits of clay have been turned into rock by the growth of mineral cements in pore spaces. Thick deposits of **clay** which consist simply of uncemented sediment are mined for brick or pottery production. These clay-rich deposits have the interesting, not to say inconvenient, ability to both absorb and lose large amounts of water — as dwellers on the sedimentary formation known as the London Clay well know. When water is scarce, clay minerals shrink, because the water molecules which fit into their structure are lost. If this happens on a large scale, ten per cent or more of the volume of some clays can disappear, perhaps through the water-seeking roots of trees — not a healthy state of affairs if your house happens to be nearby and you like your floors level.

Some people hate clays and others love them. The 'cold clay soil' from which water won't drain away is the bane of farmers and gardeners. But for precisely this reason clays are of great interest to geologists because rocks with lots of clay minerals in them can prevent water and heat (or oil and gas) from seeping away and dispersing. These properties of clay minerals have a bearing on radioactive waste containment and will be discussed in later Chapters.

Other sedimentary rocks are composed of fragments of any size, from fine **silt** — with particle sizes bigger than clay but smaller than sand — to a jumble of cobbles and boulders, these two being called, logically enough, **siltstone** and **conglomerate** respectively. Like sandstone, they may be hard and well-cemented, or soft and porous.

Not all sedimentary rocks are made up of mud or sand or pebbles cemented together. There are two other types; **evaporites** and **limestones.**

Evaporites form, as you might expect, when water evaporates. As the volume of water decreases, what is left becomes saltier. The extensive and long-term evaporation of a land-locked sea to the east of Britain, which took place a couple of hundred million years or so ago when the climate of Britain was hot and arid, has left evaporite deposits hundreds of metres thick; these are mined in North Yorkshire and South Durham. Evaporite deposits contain many different minerals, one of which is rock salt (halite) which is extracted for use on winter roads, as well as being important for the chemical industry.

The term limestone is applied to any rock which consists mainly of carbonates, usually calcium or magnesium carbonate. Many plants and animals, like the shells and some seaweeds that we find on beaches and rocky shores, leave calcium carbonate remains when they die, and thick accumulations of this material may be turned into limestone. Limestones dissolve rather easily in water, so they are not favoured for radioactive waste disposal, because long-lived radionuclides need a very stable environment if they are to remain where they are stored underground.

Rock Dimensions

To get an idea of what sort of area or volume sedimentary rocks may occupy in the geosphere it helps to remember two things. Firstly, they start off as sediments which blanket the underlying rock, which may be igneous, metamorphic or sedimentary.

Secondly, visualising a coastal plain with hills behind, or the flood plain of a large river, gives an idea of the scale on which sediments accumulate, some over large areas, some much more localised (Figure 2.7). Sedimentation is going on all the time on sea and lake floors as well. So when conditions are right (for a few million years) with a supply of sediment to an area of the Earth's crust which is slowly sinking, thick layers of sedimentary rock up to thousands of metres thick can build up in what is called a **sedimentary basin** (Figure 2.8). These basins can extend over large geographical

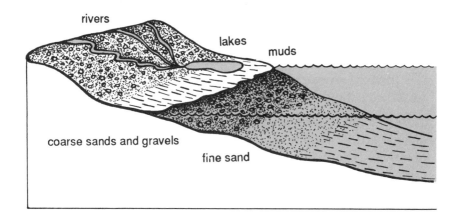

Figure 2.7 Coastal sedimentation. Sediments blanket low-lying areas and the sea floor.

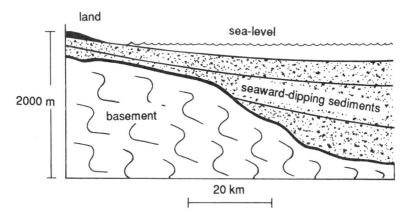

Figure 2.8 A sedimentary basin. The vertical scale is greater than the horizontal scale, so depth appears exaggerated compared with width.

areas. For instance, Dounreay, on the north coast of Caithness, and Sellafield in Cumbria both sit on the edge of ancient sedimentary basins.

The processes which cause the accumulation of sediments (the raw material for sedimentary rock) change through time at any one locality, with the result that different types of sedimentary rock pile up on top of each other, often in repeated sequences or cycles. Thus a phrase like 'seaward-dipping sediments' can refer to many different types of rock: either mainly thick sandstone units or perhaps mainly thin, alternating siltstones and mudrocks, or repeated cycles of shale/limestone/sandstone with occasional evaporites (Figure 2.9).

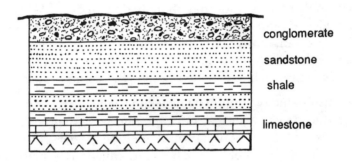

Figure 2.9 A sedimentary sequence.

We have now looked at some common rock types and their characteristic dimensions and seen how they can exist together in the geosphere. The next section looks at the transition from geosphere to biosphere through sediments and soils and the process of weathering.

Sediments and Weathering

In many parts of the country, especially in lowland areas, it is sediments of various kinds, and not rocks, which lie immediately beneath our feet (or roads and pavements). The soils in which plants can grow are no more than a few centimetres to half a metre thick and can be ignored for the moment. More significant are various muds, silts, sands, gravels, and peats as well as a range of glacial sediments left over from the last Ice Age. These are collectively known as **superficial deposits**, and may thickly blanket the rock over large areas of the land surface.

In some places sands and gravels deposited by the sea can be found inland and well above sea level, since at the end of the last Ice Age the sea level was higher relative to the land, and the sea covered more of the land than it does today. When the sea receded, coastal sands, including dunes, were left behind in what today are inland areas. There are also huge deposits of sand and gravel in places such as the Thames Valley, where rivers much larger than we know today were fed by melting glaciers.

Another kind of superficial deposit is called **drift.** This has been produced by moving glaciers or ice sheets. It may consist of thick sands and gravels laid down by melting glaciers, or it may be a mixture of clay, pebbles and boulders called **till** (sometimes called **boulder clay**) up to 50 or 60 metres thick. Drift can form mounds and hillocks as well as flat sheets, thicker where there are dips and hollows in the rock beneath. Till often has a high percentage of clay minerals and can be very heavily compacted, thus preventing water percolation except through cracks or fractures.

Weathering is the physical and chemical alteration of the minerals and rocks by the environment. Rain water can react chemically with many minerals, especially in hot climates. In cold environments, physical break-up is more common: water gets into tiny cracks in the rock and then freezes. The water expands as it turns to ice and splits the rock open. Particles thus released from the rock can be eroded and transported away by streams, rivers, wind and glaciers, and subsequently deposited to form accumulations of sediment.

In some circumstances, for instance in a hot humid climate where the land surface is low and flat, erosion may not accompany weathering. If suitable conditions continue for long enough, the weathered zone grows in thickness from the surface down, and this zone can extend to depths of forty or fifty metres; this provides an easy passageway for water through what was originally hard, crystalline rock.

It is perhaps surprising to realise that a thick weathered layer can be found *within* crystalline rock several hundred metres below ground. But geology is sometimes amenable to the 'Elementary, my dear Watson' approach. Readers who don't fancy themselves as latter-day Sherlock Holmes may wish to read the following explanation.

This is, of course, that extensive weathering occurred *before* the overlying rocks buried and preserved the weathered layer.

Landforms and Geological Structures

There are many books about geology and scenery which demonstrate how landforms closely reflect the geology; but there may also be contrasts. For instance, the land surface and the underlying rock structures may be sloping in different directions (Figure 2.10).

Figure 2.8 emphasises how the coastline does not necessarily reflect the structures in the geosphere. The seaward-dipping sediments continue uninterrupted, straight out under the sea. This is why some coal mines are off-shore — along the coasts of Northumberland and Fife for example — since coal seams are

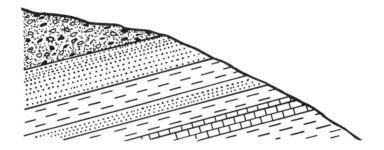

Figure 2.10 Opposing slope of land surface and rock structures.

layers which occur at intervals in some sedimentary basins. It is also, of course, the reason that one option for siting radioactive waste repositories is under the sea, but accessed from land (Chapter 9).

Rocks and Radioactive Waste Containment

The geosphere is a three-dimensional world beneath the familiar biosphere, characterised by many different rock types and structures. We can see and sample it only in patches and must use a combination of high technology and the Sherlock Holmes approach to deduce what lies between our observation points.

If rock is the containment vessel for radioactive waste, it clearly isn't as uniform or physically and chemically simple as containment vessels made of steel or concrete; neither has it a simple, consistent relationship with the biosphere. In the cooking analogy of Chapter 1, the recipe for radioactive waste disposal is getting complicated.

What's more, the 'recipe' indicates that disposing of radioactive waste in the geosphere involves water as well as rock. The study of the occurrence and behaviour of water in the geosphere and of the connections between surface water and groundwater is called **hydrogeology**.

Summary

All rocks fall into one of the three categories: igneous, metamorphic, and sedimentary. The physical extent of rock types and their juxtaposition depends on how they were formed (for instance, layered sediments or intrusive masses). In places, superficial deposits cover the ground surface to a depth of many metres, and groundwater can percolate into the rock below.

It is actually difficult to avoid groundwater in the geosphere; so the idea has evolved that groundwater could, in certain circumstances, help to restrict the movement of radionuclides away from an underground repository. This idea is known as **hydrogeological containment** of radioactive waste.

The next Chapter looks at the occurrence of groundwater, considers just why it is important in the discussion of waste containment and identifies some of the links and barriers between water in the biosphere and geosphere.

Chapter 3

Underground Fluids

If a repository is to contain radioactive waste safely for many thousands of years, we need to know exactly what fluids there would be in the vicinity of a repository, in what quantities, how they move around and where they would end up after that length of time. Confidence in geological containment depends on this knowledge and also on our ability to predict the behaviour of underground fluids in the distant future.

In the geosphere surrounding a repository, two kinds of fluid would occur — groundwater, and naturally occurring gases. In addition, there would be gases generated in the repository itself. Pressures increase with depth below ground, so repository gases may dissolve in groundwater, bubbling out again if the water enters a zone of lower pressure nearer the surface.

It is inevitable that at some point in the life of an underground radioactive waste repository, radioactive material will escape from the decaying barriers of steel and concrete within which it has been stored. The concept of geological containment is based on the belief that rocks could hold back the contamination and isolate it from the biosphere. But the geosphere doesn't have clear boundaries like the walls of a steel drum, so once the radioactivity escaped from engineered barriers into the geosphere, where would it go?

The widely accepted answer is that it would go where groundwater goes. That at least, is the simple story which we will stick to until Chapter 6, though natural systems are seldom simple. However, no-one disputes that the *principal* means of transporting radionuclides away from a deep repository would be groundwater. This is partly because water can move through the geosphere, and partly because water is a medium in which solids and gases can dissolve, and with which liquids can mix. It is also possible for fine particles of radioactive material to travel as suspended solids. In addition, chemical reactions can take place between the rocks and radionuclides in ground water.

Groundwater

If we exclude the oceans and the polar icecaps, a surprising 25% of the world's water is held in the top 1,000 metres or so of the geosphere.

Many observations confirm the presence of groundwater. For example, mines, which are large underground caverns like a nuclear waste repository, normally have to be pumped out continuously to get rid of the groundwater seeping into them. When pumping stopped during the 1986 coal miners' strike in Britain, some mines were flooded and had to be abandoned. Clearly this water isn't rain pouring down the access or ventilation shafts! It comes from within the rocks themselves.

Groundwater is often encountered in tunnels as well; major tunnels carrying roads and railways may have to be sealed very carefully against water seeping or even pouring in from the surrounding rocks. Groundwater is a major hazard during tunnelling in many geological formations, and sudden flooding has caused many tunnelling accidents. Recently, progress in the Channel Tunnel has been held up by unexpectedly large amounts of water entering the tunnel through a zone of tiny cracks.

Further evidence of the presence of underground water comes from the wells and springs which are a familiar feature of the countryside. A well contains groundwater which has collected as it seeps into the well shaft from the surrounding rock, while a spring is simply the site where circulating groundwater reaches the surface. If the water is escaping under pressure it will gush out; if not, it will simply seep out.

The boundary between surface water and groundwater is called the **water table**. This is the level in the ground below which water saturates all the available spaces in the geosphere. 'Saturation' doesn't mean that the whole geosphere is sopping wet; there may be very little water because there is very little space for it.

Groundwater Movement

Groundwater doesn't just lie passively in the spaces in rocks; it can move around the geosphere, and evidence for large-scale movement is easily found. In some areas such as the south-east of England, much of the public water supply doesn't come from surface water — that is lakes, rivers and reservoirs — but from **aquifers,** which are sedimentary rocks that may contain large volumes of slowly moving groundwater. Some countries such as Libya have no rivers or lakes whatsoever and rely entirely on groundwater for water supplies.

An aquifer is a thick layer of particularly porous rock, often sandstone or limestone, which stores water. This water can then be pumped out and used. Ideally, rain water and melted snow will seep down and **recharge** (fill up) the aquifer at the same rate as pumping depletes it. Recharge takes place in a rainy, upland area from which surface water seeps down through the underlying rock (Figure 3.1). The recharge area may be many kilometres from the point of extraction for use in a town or city — so water can obviously travel quite long distances through rocks beneath the surface.

Clearly then, groundwater movement serves to *link* the geosphere and the biosphere — an important consideration for a mined radioactive waste repository, where water (and hence radio-nuclide) transport is the enemy of containment. However, some-times underground fluids can be *isolated* from the biosphere by natural features and processes. Think of travellers in the desert who, nearly dying of thirst, dig a well with their last strength, finally hit water, but with despair find it too salty to drink. Almost certainly this water has been trapped underground for a very long time — thousands, or even tens of thousands of years — and during that time has absorbed soluble minerals (eg. rock salt) from its rock container.

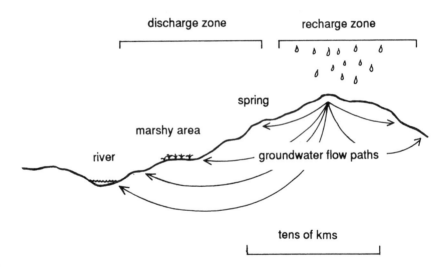

Figure 3.1 Recharge and discharge of an aquifer.

That of course is little consolation to the travellers! But it is of great interest to geologists investigating the feasibility of hydroge-ological containment of radioactive waste. It means that, at least in some circumstances, groundwater can remain isolated from the biosphere for very long periods of time.

For example, there is a good deal of evidence that most of the water below the Libyan desert percolated into the geosphere between 35,000 and 15,000 years ago during a wet, rainy period. Today, the climate of Libya is so dry that it is unlikely that the aquifer could be recharged. The recharge area for the central Libyan desert aquifer was, and is, the Tibesti mountains which lie to the south-west. Water takes thousands of years to travel so far, and during all this time, of course, the water has remained isolated from the biosphere.

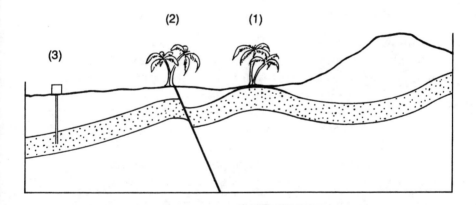

Figure 3.2 A desert aquifer. Groundwater can find pathways to the surface where the aquifer is exposed (1) or up a fault (2), and thus form oases. It can also remain isolated from the biosphere (3).

There are natural as well as artificial means of breaking this isolation. A geological **fault** is a break on either side of which rocks have been displaced relative to each other. A fault may extend hundreds of metres below the surface. Figure 3.2 shows a fault intersecting an aquifer and allowing groundwater to seep upwards and form an oasis. If a natural link between aquifer and ground surface is absent, the only way to get water to the surface would be by drilling a well.

Oil wells provide another example of isolation of underground fluids from the biosphere. Oil, often accompanied by water and gas, is trapped underground, usually because its progress to the surface is barred by a layer of impermeable rock such as shale or rock salt. Impermeable rock is more or less waterproof, or rather oilproof, and the oil can stay there for tens of millions of years until a drilling rig pierces the trap.

Groundwater Movement and Waste Containment

Groundwater circulates in the geosphere and would circulate through and around a radioactive waste repository. If circulation is slow, restricted in area, well-understood, predictable with a high degree of confidence and stable over very long periods of time, the radioactive waste might be effectively contained. If circulation is on a large scale, difficult to observe and test, imperfectly understood, poorly predictable and liable to be altered by natural or human intrusion, it could be impossible to prevent the dispersal of radioactive waste over a wide area.

A number of mistaken assumptions about the effect of circulating groundwater on radioactive waste containment have already been made in European countries, the USA and the USSR. For instance, the storage of LLW and ILW in an abandoned salt mine at Bartensleben near the East German border has led to measurable radioactivity in river water at Helmstedt across the border in

West Germany. In the USA, widespread contamination of soils and groundwater has led to the closure of shallow LLW dumps. Out of nine sites opened in the USA since the end of the last war, only two (in desert areas) have shown no release of radionuclides (Milnes, 1985).

A final point to note is that the presence of groundwater does not necessarily mean that there is an active circulation system linking biosphere and geosphere, because not all groundwater is derived from rainfall. Three other sources of groundwater are the magma (molten rock) which rises from deep within the Earth and solidifies to form igneous rocks, releasing some water in the process; the water squeezed out of sediments as they are buried, compressed and turned into rock in the recent or distant past; and chemically bound water released from clay minerals as they are buried and heated up.

Summary

There is evidence that:

* water and gas occur naturally in the geosphere.

* in some circumstances fluids move through rocks.

* in some circumstances rocks trap fluids underground.

* fluids can move from the geosphere to the biosphere and vice versa.

* groundwater can move very slowly or quite rapidly.

Obviously no-one would want to build a radioactive waste repository anywhere near springs or aquifers where fast-flowing water is used by people. Indeed, such areas would be actively avoided. However, geologists are well aware that groundwater may be present as much as 1,500 metres below the surface and that repository design would have to allow for some degree of groundwater flow. The absence of groundwater is unusual and while groundwater could contribute to the escape of radioactive materials it could also be involved in processes leading to short-term or long-term containment.

Understanding the arguments about whether a repository would be safe involves understanding how groundwater moves and this is the subject of the next two Chapters. First of all Chapter 4 describes the spaces in rocks — the fractures, pores and various natural gaps that disrupt much 'solid' rock. Then, in Chapter 5, the distribution of these water-containing spaces is related to groundwater circulation patterns involving both biosphere and geosphere.

Chapter 4

Pores and Fractures

As we have seen, 'solid rock' isn't uniformly solid, since it contains pores, fractures and fissures of various kinds, which are formed by natural processes. Groundwater occupies these spaces.

Six common kinds of spaces in solid rock are described in turn below. The odd ones out in this group — but none the less important for that — are pores, since all the others are features which cut across other geological boundaries. They are:

- **fractures** which are irregular in direction and/or distribution and are often associated with crystalline rock

- **joints** (regular sets of fractures commonly found in many rock types)

- **bedding planes** (in sedimentary and some volcanic rocks)

- **unconformities** (between rocks of distinct age and type)

- **faults** (in any type of rock)

- **pores** (mainly in sedimentary rocks)

Any type of rock can be split or broken apart if stresses are large enough. Spaces are formed when compression or stretching of parts of the Earth's crust occurs; when deeply buried rock or magma which has been at high temperatures cools and shrinks; when a large rock body such as a granite forces its way up into the pre-existing country rock; or in response to pressure release as deeply buried rocks rise to the surface. Igneous, metamorphic and sedimentary rocks can all be disrupted in this way.

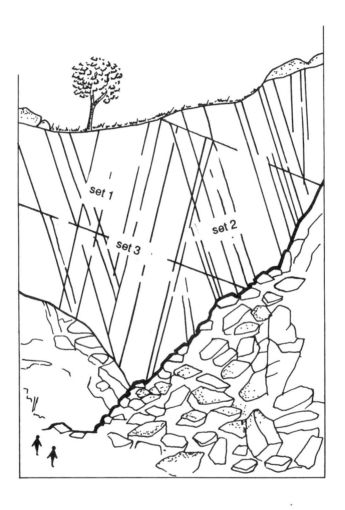

Figure 4.1 Intersecting joint sets in a quarry face.

Fractures

The word **fracture** or fissure is often used in a general way to indicate various kinds of breaks in rocks.

Fractures may be very large features — several kilometres in length — caused by major movements within the geosphere, sometimes occurring in wide fracture zones; or they may be tiny fractures, perhaps only thousandths of a millimetre across. Small fractures may appear to be randomly oriented, but within larger fracture zones, distinct patterns can usually be detected. This is because fracturing is a response to forces acting on the rock from well-defined directions. Some fractures may radiate out from a central zone, for instance where a pluton has intruded; others may be vertical and run approximately East–West; yet others could be more or less parallel to the ground surface and run more North–South. Several sets of intersecting fractures can co-exist when the rock has undergone several different episodes of stress during a long geological history.

Joints

Joints are regular sets of fractures spaced at anything from 10 centimetres to 10 metres apart. Within a joint set, they are often parallel to each other, but they may also have other geometrical relationships (Figure 4.1). They can be at any angle to the ground surface and two or three intersecting joint sets are commonly found together. Joints can be anything from a metre to tens of metres long and may be even longer, although not continuous. Joints and fractures are distinguished from fault planes (see below) by the fact that the break in the rock has not been accompanied by relative movement of the rock on either side.

The extraordinary basalt columns of the Giant's Causeway in Northern Ireland are the result of the development of joints during solidification and contraction of the basalt lava, though no doubt not many visitors are too bothered by this fact which rather spoils the fairy stories. The patterns in the rock are caused by vertical joints running at different, intersecting angles.

Rock layers

As sediments accumulate, they form distinct layers, each one of which is formed of more or less the same kind of sediment. However, any one layer may be made of a different kind of sediment from the adjacent layers. These separate layers are called **beds**, and the boundaries between the layers are called **bedding planes.** Another name for a bed is a stratum (plural: strata). Layering like this can also form in some kinds of volcanic rocks. Hence the plane surface separating each bed of sedimentary rock in Figure 2.9 is a bedding plane.

Most bedding planes are originally roughly horizontal, corresponding to the flat topography of areas such as river valleys, shorelines and estuaries. But movements of the Earth's crust can fold and tilt sedimentary rocks so that the bedding planes end up at any angle between horizontal and vertical (Figure 2.10). Since bedding planes are boundaries between different kinds of rock such as shale and sandstone, they may provide pathways for groundwater flow.

Unconformities

An **unconformity** is a boundary between rocks of very different ages and is given that name because the rocks above and below the boundary are quite unrelated; they do not 'conform'.

The difference in ages between rocks on either side of an unconformity can be hundreds of millions of years, during which time the surface of the older rock was eroded and weathered (Figure 4.2).

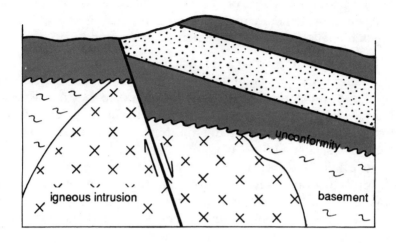

Figure 4.2 An unconformity which separates crystalline basement rocks from younger sedimentary rocks above. The unconformity is displaced by a fault; the rocks on the right-hand side have gone down relative to those on the left.

Unconformities can be significant in hydrogeology; for example, if a porous weathered zone (through which groundwater can move relatively easily) has developed at the top of the lower sequence of rocks, and is then covered by younger rocks, the weathered zone can offer a concealed pathway for groundwater.

Faults

A fault is a break on either side of which the rocks have been displaced relative to each other. The zone of movement is called the fault plane. Both the amount of displacement and the direction of displacement are variable.

Faulting can move the blocks of rock on opposite sides of the fault plane up and down and/or sideways relative to each other. The amount of movement can be anything from centimetres to hundreds of metres, or even kilometres in some cases.

Faults can occur in any type of rock and cut across all other rock boundaries such as bedding planes or unconformities. Sets of roughly parallel, related faults are common and they may extend laterally for tens or hundreds of kilometres. They may reach down from the ground surface many hundreds of metres, as shown in the cross-section of the geology of the land to the east of Sellafield (Figure 2.5). This diagram also shows how some faults don't reach the present ground surface. Many faults remain undiscovered for this reason, and the important part they can play in groundwater circulation means that looking for concealed faults is a vital part of site investigation for a waste repository.

The shape of coastlines can often be determined by faults because the weakened rock in the fault planes is more easily eroded and washed away by the sea and streams to form bays and inlets.

A fault often produces a zone of disruption which can be anything between centimetres or tens of metres wide. Within this zone the rock may be crushed, ground up, or severely fractured, providing an easy route for water movement. In other cases, such as the fractured shale in Cornwall investigated by Nirex (Lever, 1989), surprisingly little water flow is observed.

There are also circumstances in which faults can *prevent* fluid circulation and these are discussed in Chapter 5. Faults are large-scale features and are very common. Hence it is important to be able to predict, for each site under investigation for radioactive waste disposal, whether individual faults will allow or obstruct the passage of groundwater. This is an under-researched and difficult task (Black *et al*, 1987).

Porosity and permeability

Pores are the spaces between the cemented fragments which form a sedimentary rock (Figure 2.2). On a sandy beach where the tide has just gone out and the sand is damp, 40% to 60% of the volume of the sand is likely to be pore space filled with water because the grains are not tightly packed. If the sediment is buried and turns into rock, the grains will be forced closer together and carbonate or silica cement will fill some of the remaining pore space. The porosity of sedimentary rock is usually between 2% and 25%.

Some volcanic rocks can be quite porous too; the pores are actually little holes left in rapidly solidifying magma as bubbles of gas escaped from it. An extreme example is pumice which is so full of little holes that it is really just a rock soufflé. Pores in some other volcanic rocks are often filled with different minerals deposited from groundwater long after the rock itself was formed.

Since most rocks in the top few hundred metres of the geosphere are saturated with water, a simple calculation can give us a feel for the amount of groundwater which could exist in a pile of sedimentary rocks.

In a zone of sedimentary rocks 10 kilometres wide, 10 kilometres long and on average 400 metres (0.4 kilometres) thick how much water *could* there be? The answer depends on the proportion of the volume of the rock which is pore space, that is, the **porosity** of the rock. Porosity may be very variable at different depths and at different distances from any observation point, but for simplicity let's suppose that:

The rock has a porosity of 5%, and the rock is saturated with water. So 5% of the rock volume is water-filled pores. The volume of the water in this example is therefore 5% of the volume of the rock.

To calculate the volume of the rock multiply width x length x depth:

Volume = 10km x 10km x 0.4km = 40 cubic km

and then multiply this volume by 5% ie. five hundredths:

Water-filled pore volume = 40 x 5/100 = 2 cubic km

The calculation shows that in this zone of the geosphere there are two cubic kilometres of water. Of course not all this water will be on the move; there may be stagnant zones or it may be trapped in tiny, tortuous or isolated pores. It will certainly not flow evenly through the whole volume of rock since it invariably takes the easiest way out: this may be through interconnected pores and/ or through joints and fractures. The rate at which fluids can travel through a body of rock is called the **permeability** of the rock. Permeability is measured in metres per second.

Small though pores are, if they are interconnected and the rock is thus made permeable, they may make a very significant contribution to the presence of groundwater and allow it to travel long distances within sedimentary basins.

Metamorphic rock has virtually no pores because, in common with most igneous rocks such as granite, it is formed of interlocking mineral crystals which have grown together to form a tight mass. As a result, water travels through crystalline rock mainly via fractures, whereas in sedimentary rock it can travel through pores and along bedding planes as well as along the various types of fractures.

Thus the presence or absence of interconnected spaces and fractures of various kinds determines whether rocks are permeable or impermeable. If something is impermeable it is effectively waterproof — it doesn't let water (or gases) pass through it. For instance, a zone of granite with tightly closed microfractures would be impermeable. So would a thick bed of shale consisting largely of clay minerals, because the clay particles are so tiny that many pores are too small and tortuous for water movement. In other cases, there may be large pores, but not enough connections between them for water to penetrate the rock continuously. Bathroom pumice stone is a porous but impermeable rock of this kind. The numerous pores mean that it is air-filled and very light, and it floats in the bath because the lack of connections between the pores means that it doesn't become water-logged. A crystalline rock would have low permeability, too, if any fractures were widely spaced or poorly interconnected.

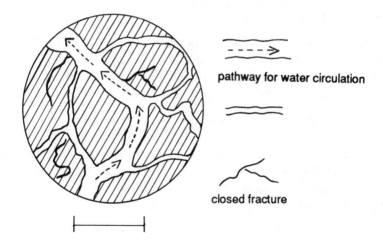

pathway for water circulation

closed fracture

Figure 4.3 Microfissures in a rock. Scale bar one twentieth of a millimetre.

However, even in impermeable shale or crystalline rock, extremely slow movement of substances *is* possible by a process called diffusion, which allows transfer of water and gas from one mineral grain to the next. Diffusion is only significant over very long periods of time, but may be relevant in considering disposal of long-lived radioactive wastes. Diffusion can take place for instance in microfissures, as illustrated in Figure 4.3, and may also be an important means of transporting substances in impermeable clay-rich rocks (see Chapter 6).

Another term often used in discussions of groundwater is **hydraulic conductivity**. This relates the permeability of the rock to the volume of water which can flow through a given area in a given time. Rocks which have a hydraulic conductivity of less than one litre of water per square metre per day are generally regarded as impermeable. However, when dealing with permeability, it is useful to remember that all things are relative; impermeable does not mean 'totally waterproof'.

If you knew the hydraulic conductivity of the rock in which a radioactive waste repository was to be built, and you also knew the area of the walls of the caverns, you could calculate how much water would enter the repository every day (or year, or century).

Laboratory tests show that unfractured samples of crystalline rock may have very low hydraulic conductivities, perhaps about one hundredth of a litre (a couple of teaspoons) per square metre per day. This is one reason why crystalline rock, free from major fractures, has been much studied with radioactive waste disposal in mind.

However, there are difficulties in assuming that what happens in a laboratory test will apply in a simple way to the real world; the change of scale from a small laboratory sample to a mined underground cavity introduces new features, in particular fractures large and small. To take an actual example: at the former

Stripa iron mine in central Sweden an international research project into radioactive waste disposal in fractured crystalline rock has been conducted (Milnes, 1985). Because rock is variable stuff, the hydraulic conductivity varies from zone to zone, but an average is about one tenth of a litre per square metre per day (ten times higher than the laboratory sample). However the mine also contains deep fracture zones which have a hydraulic conductivity of more than ten litres per square metre per day — more than a thousand times greater than the laboratory sample.

Sedimentary rocks generally have much higher hydraulic conductivities than crystalline rocks, because water can move through pores as well as fractures. In the top few hundred metres of the St. Bees Sandstone which lies beneath the Sellafield nuclear complex (Figure 2.5), hydraulic conductivity is typically at least a thousand times greater than in crystalline rock (Nirex Report No. 71, 1989). The reason is that the water finds its way through a combination of interconnected systems of pores, joints and fault zones which make the rock quite permeable. Well-cemented sandstones have low porosity and many fewer connections between pores. They can thus be rather impermeable. However, it is normal for porosity and fracturing to vary widely both laterally and vertically, making it difficult to generalise about hydraulic conductivity over large zones.

Whatever the rock type, hydrualic conductivity is rarely the same when measured vertically and horizontally. This property is called **anisotropy**. For instance, shales can conduct water much more easily parallel to the bedding plains; shales are therefore described as highly anisotropic (Figure 4.4(a)). Igneous rock like granite will also be hydraulically anisotropic if it contains a series of major vertical joints or faults, because water will take the easiest route and tend to concentrate its movement in the vertical pathways.

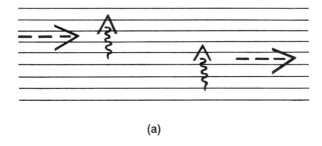

(a)

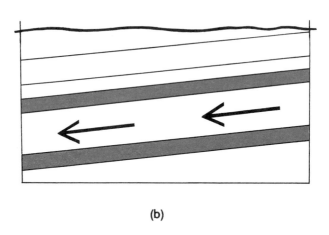

(b)

Figure 4.4 (a) Anisotropic flow in shales. Flow is severely restricted across the layers, but occurs more readily along them. (b) Anisotropic flow in a permeable layer bounded by impermeable layers.

In a sedimentary basin with sediments dipping seawards from the coast, **hydraulic anisotropy** would direct the flow downwards and away from the land (Figure 4.4(b); hence the interest in sedimentary basins for radioactive waste disposal.

Because the conditions which determine hydraulic conductivity are so dependent on the precise geological nature of the rocks, it is extremely difficult to generalise about their ability to transmit fluids, and large variations within a single rock type are also common. In the context of radioactive waste disposal, it may be a good starting point for research to say that, in general, very little water flows through fractured hard rock, but only detailed investigation will reveal whether general rules apply at a particular site.

Wet and Dry Fractures

Not all available fractures in rocks actually transmit groundwater. In considering radioactive waste containment, we need to know whether the joints and fractures are:

- closed or open
- closely or widely spaced
- wide or narrow
- interconnected
- long or short
- widespread or confined to a small area
- arranged in a random or regular pattern
- straight or tortuous

It is these features (as well as the pressure of the water or gas) which determine whether fractures are 'wet' or 'dry', that is whether or not they can transmit fluids.

For example, it is common for the walls of fractures to be so tightly forced together that not even the thinnest possible layer of water, even under the high pressures which exist in the geosphere, can get through. In other cases, the gap between the walls may be sealed by minerals which grew there after the break was formed. In such cases the term closed fractures is often used.

Other fractures are open and are able to transmit groundwater because the stresses acting on the rocks allow the walls of the fractures to remain apart or because no minerals have filled the gaps. A third possibility is that minerals previously filling fractures have been partly dissolved away by groundwater which was, or is, circulating through them.

A useful rule of thumb is that fractures are wider and more frequently open nearer the surface, and narrower and more often closed at greater depth (below about two or three hundred metres). Where this is the case, there will be smaller volumes of groundwater and slower groundwater movement at greater depths. However, it is just a rule of thumb and there are many exceptions. For instance, significant amounts of groundwater have been recorded in mines in metamorphic rock in Canada at depths of more than 1,000 metres (Price, 1985). This is near the maximum depth for the construction of a radioactive waste repository.

Closer to home, geologists from the British Geological Survey did extensive work on the fractured hard rock in the Altnabreac area of Caithness (see Figure 1.2) in the early 1980's as part of a research project on HLW disposal. They concluded from analyses of 300 metre deep boreholes that it was not safe to assume that the number of open fractures would steadily decrease at greater depths (McEwen and Lintern, 1980). What they found was that zones of intense fracturing, with many open fractures, sometimes appeared suddenly more than two hundred metres down, below an area where the number of closed fractures had been steadily increasing with depth. In other words, there was no steady trend from open fractures near the surface to more and more closed fractures at depth.

So if it is important to site a repository where groundwater flow is minimal, mining deeper and deeper isn't necessarily the answer. At some sites the rule of thumb may apply, at others it may not. The fracture pattern at Altnabreac consisted of fracture zones tens of metres in width, possibly continuous over more than one kilometre in length and present at depths of over 200 metres. (No samples below 300 metres were obtained.) These mainly vertical fracture zones make the rock at this site very hydrogeologically anisotropic (McEwen and Lintern, 1980).

Looking for Patterns

One of the aims of a site investigation is to gain enough knowledge to predict what is going on in the large zones of the geosphere between direct observation points (such as boreholes and mined excavations) and also to predict future processes and events. Predictions can only be made if patterns of features and processes are observed and understood as repetitive or changing in systematic ways. It is interesting to note, however, how the *scale* and *angle* of observation may alter what is observed.

On a small scale a fracture pattern may seem random; but on a larger scale a general trend may be seen. So it is important that experiments and observations designed to find out about fractures, and hence groundwater movement through and around a repository, are done on the right scale. What happens in a small piece of rock in a laboratory, or in a single fracture in the wall of an underground research site in a field experiment, may not represent the wider geosphere very well. A case in point is the study of clays and shales, samples of which are inevitably disturbed by the time they reach the laboratory (Lever, 1989).

However, experiments at an underground research site at Mol in Belgium are being designed to investigate this problem.

The angle as well as the scale of observation is important. Having found a pattern, researchers must ask what the view from a different angle would be. The geosphere has to be represented in three dimensions; this point may seem obvious, but it is worth making, since two- or even one-dimensional representations of the geosphere are often used in research work and give rise to the frequent criticism that there are more computerised representations (models) of what would happen to radionuclides in a repository than there are reliable data on which to base them.

A third problem in looking for patterns in the geosphere can be illustrated by imagining that there are variations in the frequency of fractures. Direct samples of the geosphere can only be taken in the form of **cores** which are perhaps 10 centimetres in diameter and taken from widely-spaced boreholes.

However, boreholes may give an unrealistic picture of the frequency of fractures and their orientation. Figure 4.5 shows typical cores from boreholes in fractured rock. Cores may intersect very few fractures if on average the fractures are spaced more than 10 centimetres apart (the width of the core). On this basis, a quite false picture of the fracture density and hydraulic conductivity could emerge.

So the problem in looking for significant patterns is one of generalising from very limited samples, and the way this obliges researchers to assume the geosphere is simple and uniform when in fact it is not. With difficulties, or to look at it another way, challenges, of this kind to contend with, most geologists are cautious about relying on any one set of data even if it appears to be quite unequivocal. Naturally, efforts are made to site boreholes where experience and knowledge of the local geology suggest crucial information will be found. The snag is that obviously we

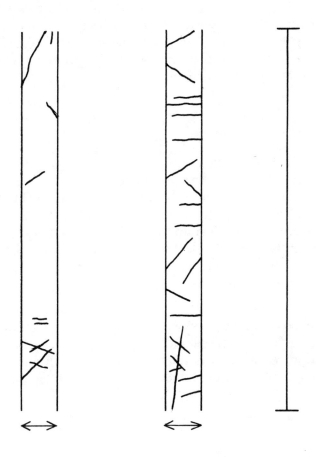

Figure 4.5 Sketches of typical cores from boreholes in fractured rock. Is the left-hand core more or less unfractured, or is it riddled with vertical fractures more than 10 centimetres apart? Is the right-hand core really dominated by horizontal fractures? Vertical scale bar 10 metres, horizontal scale bars 10 centimetres.

cannot anticipate the unexpected. Because of the extent and inaccessibility of the geosphere, the discovery of significant but unexpected features can lead to further problems. Of course, this is not an argument against research but a strong argument in favour of extensive and imaginative research.

Summary

This Chapter has outlined the nature of pores and various linear features in rocks. Fractures may be open (allowing the passage of fluids) or closed (cemented by mineral growth or held shut by pressure). Rocks are permeable when open pores and fissures are interconnected. The local and regional distribution of groundwater pathways controls the direction and rate at which groundwater can flow, but there are difficult problems to overcome in reaching a good understanding of significant patterns.

We have looked at why and where fluids are to be found in the geosphere. The next Chapter discusses the patterns and scale of groundwater circulation as well as circumstances in which hydrogeological containment of radioactive waste could operate.

Chapter 5

Groundwater Circulation and Hydrogeological Containment

The last two Chapters have established, firstly that the geosphere contains variable amounts of water, and secondly, that there are different kinds of space in 'solid rock' through which fluids can move with greater or lesser ease.

Since groundwater flow is likely to be the major cause of migration of radionuclides away from a repository, we have to consider how it can establish links between geosphere and biosphere.

In contrast, the concept of **hydrogeological containment** depends upon the idea that groundwater can *prevent* radionuclides migrating away from an underground repository.

Circulation Patterns

Most hydrogeological research has naturally been done for commercial reasons, concentrating on plentiful supplies of underground water. Some well-known examples of underground water circulation are provided by spa waters. For example, in the city of Bath, rain falling on the Mendip Hills percolates down into an aquifer, travels north east for about 25 kilometres having reached depths of over 2,000 metres, and finally rises rather rapidly up a fault system to provide the famous waters (Figure 5.1)

The once-glorious Victorian spa at Strathpeffer in Ross and Cromarty is another example of the way that groundwater circulation delivers the goods (nauseatingly sulphurous from the bacterial decomposition of organic matter in shales), this time via a much smaller, **local flow**. The source of the water is the high ground immediately above the village. The water percolates down through the rocks before reaching the surface again at the fault in the valley floor where the village lies, and where a series of springs used to feed a line of collecting tanks for the spa water.

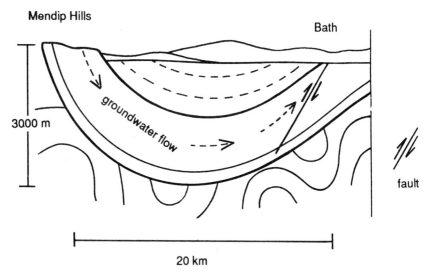

Figure 5.1 Sketch section of the source of the Bath Spa waters.

These examples indicate that groundwater does circulate over quite large distances and that rapid upward movement may be related to faulting. Such zones of rapid flow would not, of course, be appropriate for a radioactive waste repository. Slow, restricted circulation would provide conditions in which containment would be more likely to work.

In the geosphere, lateral and vertical changes in pressure and temperature give rise to systematically changing conditions which cause water to flow. The greater the changes, the faster the water will move.

Water movement in aquifers through pores and fissures may be quite rapid, perhaps several metres per day, though it is important not to imagine that the water flows in underground rivers. In contrast, deep groundwater in impermeable rock might take a year to travel one metre or less, and it is only in the case of long-lived toxic waste disposal that this rate of flow becomes significant.

Some of the water precipitated on to the Earth's surface doesn't run off straight into lakes, rivers or the sea. Instead it percolates downwards through pores and fractures in rock to join existing groundwater, before moving upwards to the surface again to feed a body of surface water. How deep it goes depends on the pressure and temperature differences; the greater these are, the deeper it is likely to travel. Water from the Earth's surface can penetrate to depths of 1,000 metres or more in hilly areas.

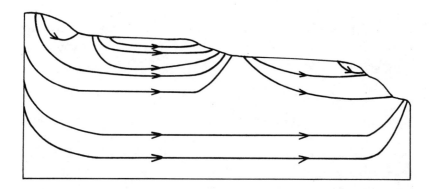

Figure 5.2 The effect of topography on ground-water circulation.

Groundwater circulation cells are often produced by topographic features such as hills and valleys (Figure 5.2), and the resultant flow patterns are not easily predicted from first principles (Chapman and McKinley, 1987). Where the ground surface is flatter, circulation patterns are simpler. This is why flat, low-lying ground is considered desirable for a repository.

Not all groundwater has percolated down from the surface in the recent past and different circulation systems often exist at different depths. These are likely to include:

* small, local systems with 'young' water which closely reflect short-term variations in precipitation at the surface

* large-scale flows of 'old' water

* systems (including any of the two above) which contain various proportions of 'old' and 'young' water.

There are also zones where water can be trapped in dead-end pores and fractures, or where the flow rate becomes very small.

Techniques which allow the age and source of groundwater to be measured will be discussed in Chapter 10. However, the occurrence of flow systems which contain a mixture of young and old water is evidence that links between deep groundwater and surface water do exist.

Groundwater movement at Altnabreac, Caithness

While the theory of groundwater circulation is reasonably straightforward, sorting out what is going on in a particular part of the geosphere is not necessarily easy. Geologists looked at various aspects of groundwater at the Altnabreac research site in Caithness (Chapter 4) in the late 1970's and came up with as many questions as answers.

Studies of water chemistry suggested that even in this rather flat landscape, surface water rapidly penetrated to depths of over 160 metres. On the other hand, near the bottom of one 300 metre deep borehole, the groundwater was judged to have been there for about 10,000 years, having percolated down through the rock at the end of the last Ice Age (Kay and Bath, 1982).

Just to confuse matters, water from a third borehole, also nearly 300 metres deep, was found to contain a mixture of young and old water, indicating that a deep, largely stagnant, circulation system was in places linked to the surface and the biosphere. The clue as to how this happened was the presence of dissolved iron in the deep water. This had probably been dissolved out of minerals in the near-vertical fracture zones cutting the area, so the fractures were almost certainly acting as significant pathways for ground-water flow.

Of course, at Altnabreac only three 300 metre deep boreholes were made several kilometres apart, so we can only draw tentative conclusions about the nature of the groundwater circulation. But this study does provide a good, practical demonstration of the gap between the theory of hydrogeological containment and the business of demonstrating that it works at any particular site — in this particular case, even after four years' work by a team of knowledgeable and skilled researchers.

It is clear, therefore, that investigating a circulation system in the kind of detail necessary to predict long-term isolation of radioactivity means lengthy research. General statements about hydrogeology simply provide a starting point for such research and can guide site selection only in broad outline, especially in cases such as Sellafield and Dounreay where the deep geology was poorly known in advance. So it is not possible to say in advance of detailed site investigation that 'Groundwater circulation at this site is such that hydrogeological containment will operate.'

Effects of repository construction on groundwater

The construction of a repository would itself significantly affect groundwater circulation. Water cannot be allowed to flow into the site during construction and operation — which for a deep UK repository would be around fifty years. Mining and engineering geologists are familiar with a variety of water removal techniques such as draining water into sumps (collecting points) at the lowest part of an excavation and pumping it out to the surface from there. Particularly troublesome 'leaky' areas of fractured rock can be grouted or lined with concrete. So in the short term (a few decades) established circulation patterns would be severely disturbed.

After about fifty years, when a repository had been filled in and closed, groundwater would gradually saturate the loose backfill in the former caverns and tunnels in which the waste had been stored. To what extent the original circulation pattern would be restored, after the excavation of millions of cubic metres of rock, cessation of pumping and backfilling with different materials, is uncertain.

Two further aspects of groundwater circulation — the scale and the rate — are considered in more detail below, since both are particularly important for radioactive waste containment.

The Scale of Groundwater Circulation

If water is the main agent for transporting radionuclides away from a repository, it follows that groundwater circulation patterns determine the dispersal of radionuclides and where they would eventually emerge.

The size and shape of a **regional flow** system is controlled by the overall hydrogeological anisotropy. In other words, the differences between horizontal and vertical hydraulic conductivity values determine whether groundwater flow is predominantly horizontal, or up and down. Figures 5.3(a) and (b) illustrate how this works. Horizontal fractures tend to be tightly closed because of the great pressure of the overlying rocks. Vertical fractures are

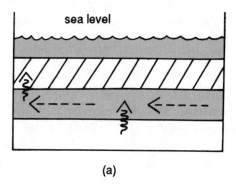

(a)

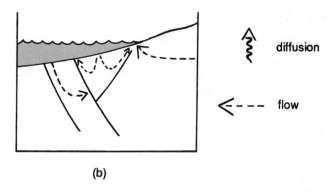

(b)

Figure 5.3 Control of flow patterns by regional anisotropy. (a) In an unfaulted sedimentary sequence, flow is mainly along the layers. (b) In faulted rock (crystalline or sedimentary), flow is mainly vertical.

more likely to remain open. If vertical flow dominates, flow systems will be relatively local and small-scale and water will be transferred from geosphere to biosphere quite rapidly. If flow is mainly horizontal, flow paths will be much longer and probably slower.

Local circulation

Small-scale systems with rapid return of groundwater to the biosphere are found near the surface in highly permeable rocks or sediments — not an environment envisaged for a radioactive waste repository for precisely this reason. But small, local flow systems may also develop in two other sets of circumstances. The presence of frequent near-vertical faults may prevent large-scale regional flow developing, with each wet fault forming the boundary of a smaller flow system which recirculates water rapidly to the biosphere. This might also create unsuitable conditions for a repository (Figure 5.3(b)).

Secondly, small flows commonly develop below small hills and irregularities in the ground surface (Figure 5.2). Where these are numerous and the rocks are permeable, they can dominate the hydrogeology, making regional flow less significant. The practical consequences for radioactive waste disposal could be that migrating radionuclides were carried shorter distances and returned more rapidly to the biosphere. It is partly for this reason that sites in flat-lying areas are considered desirable. In addition, investigating lots of small, possibly interacting, flow systems is more difficult than taking a broad, regional view and thus being able to ignore local irregularities.

On the other hand, the presence of a highly permeable fault not far from a repository might even, in theory, be an advantage. Since groundwater takes the easy way out, the concentration of flow within a fault plane could mean reduced flow in surrounding rock. In this case the fault could act as an active barrier protecting a zone of reduced groundwater flow suitable for a repository. But until we improve the limited knowledge we have of the effects that faults have on groundwater circulation (Black *et al*, 1986), it will be difficult to test such theories effectively. Caution about predicting the long term future of groundwater circulation is another argument against siting a repository near a rapid flow system, which could have a more significant effect than slow-moving water if anything did go wrong.

Regional Circulation

If the scale of groundwater circulation involving a repository is large, there is a chance that it will carry escaped radionuclides for long distances underground thus ensuring a longer residence time for both groundwater and radionuclides. This is one of the principal arguments for deep disposal. It is the large size of sedimentary basins and the resulting long circulation pathways (tens of kilometres), carrying water initially to great depths, which account for the designation of seaward-dipping sedimentary rocks as potential hosts for a repository. Nevertheless, according to the 1988 report of the House of Commons Radioactive Waste Management Committee, Britain is the only country in the world which includes off-shore sedimentary rocks in its list of possible sites for a deep radioactive waste repository. Note also that the distance travelled by radionuclides might be significantly less than the distance travelled by circulating groundwater. This important distinction is largely a matter of chemistry and is dealt with in Chapter 6.

Small Islands

Another situation where hydrogeological containment might work is in the small-scale circulation pattern associated with some small islands (Figure 5.4). In this case, local circulation is seen as a positive advantage. Rock type and permeability are less important than the restricted groundwater flow path which would, in theory, prevent radionuclides migrating away from the island (Chapman *et al*, 1986). One difficulty with this theory is that research into the effectiveness of the boundary between salt and fresh water as a barrier to regional flow is at an early stage, and has not been adequately tested (Saunders, 1988; Lever, 1989).

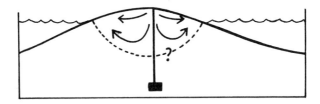

Figure 5.4 Restricted circulation beneath a small island.

We know that sea water intrusion into groundwater beneath islands and coasts modifies flow patterns because the rocks below sea level are saturated with sea water in the same way that rocks on land are saturated with fresh water. If a repository is *below* the salt/fresh water boundary beneath a small island (or off-shore), migrating radionuclides should, in theory, be trapped in the salt water at depth and be unable to reach the biosphere.

However, mixing of salt and fresh groundwater beneath small islands is also known to occur. The island of Tenerife provides an example. So many tourists now visit the island at times of low rainfall that the aquifers (which are the only source of water) are sometimes in danger of having water extracted faster than they can be replenished by rainfall. When this happens, the fresh water can become slightly salty as sea water is drawn into the system and mixes with it.

The extent to which a sharp division between salt and fresh groundwater beneath an island or coastal site could interrupt regional groundwater flow and prevent early return of radionuclides to the biosphere is not yet clear. Regional circulation would, in theory, determine the migration route, but pathways which terminate on the sea bed are particularly difficult to investigate. It is worth noting that both potential UK repository sites are coastal. The presence of a salt water barrier could make groundwater flow paths significantly shorter than they would otherwise be, since flow that would have continued out under the sea would then emerge near the coast (Lever, 1989). This might mean, of course, that radionuclides can reach the biosphere more quickly than they would otherwise have done.

Circulation in Fractured Hard Rock

When it comes to fractured hard rock, discovering and predicting flow paths, circulation patterns and scale is another challenging task. Experiments indicate that flow is strongly channelled; that is, it is restricted to specific zones and is not distributed evenly through the rock (Figure 5.5). Field investigations into channelled flow are necessarily on a small scale and there are also uncertainties about whether experiments lasting at best a few months can provide data which accurately represent what happens to slow-moving groundwater over periods of many years.

The difficulty of simulating field conditions in the laboratory means that the majority of investigations into circulation in fractured hard rock have either been computer studies based on

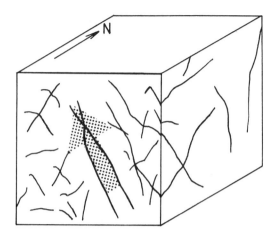

Figure 5.5 Channelled flow in fractured hard rock.

approximate data (Chapter 11) or limited field observations designed to provide some better data to feed into the computer programmes.

There is, however, a fractured hard rock repository for LLW and ILW already in operation at Forsmark in Sweden. It lies 50 metres below the bed of the Baltic Sea in granitic rock, one kilometre from the coastline. It has a volume of about 430,000 cubic metres (less than a thirtieth the size of the proposed Nirex facility). Into it seeps about 900 cubic metres of water every day, indicating that the repository lies in the path of an active groundwater circulation system. At present the water is collected and used for fire protection and heating, but when the repository is sealed and a modified flow resumes, this 900 cubic metres of groundwater a day, together with any migrating radionuclides, will rejoin the flow system.

Nevertheless the Swedes are confident about their predictions of long-term, hydrogeological containment. Containment is expected to operate because of a limited, slow flow through the crystalline rock and a barrier of salt water preventing contamination of the local flow system. Radioactivity that does escape will be diluted and dispersed in the sea, and it has been estimated that this will only add a few percent to natural background radiation.

Flow Rates

If groundwater circulates slowly it will stay underground for a long time. Conversely, rapid circulation may mean a short stay in the geosphere. **Residence time** is the length of time that water stays in one place before moving to another. For instance, the water in the Libyan desert aquifer mentioned in Chapter 2 has a residence time of about 35,000 years. Likewise, some groundwater at Altnabreac seems to have a residence time of 10,000 years. In local, small-scale flows, residence time may be only a few days before the water re-emerges in springs, marshes or stream beds. For instance, in the Isles of Scilly, where all water comes from wells, residence time is a few months, as can be only too clearly demonstrated when a dry winter fails to replenish the aquifer and water is running low by mid-summer.

Residence time is an important idea because the longer the residence time of groundwater at a repository site, the lower will be the radioactivity of any water which finally reaches the biosphere.

Unfortunately it would be rash to assume that all groundwater involved in a large scale flow system would only reach the surface again after a very long time. A combination of a high rate of supply and high hydraulic conductivity would produce the opposite effect. Such a combination could be found in permeable rocks in an upland area — the Mendip Hills provide a good example (Figure 5.1). For these reasons, low relief, such as is found in coastal areas, and minimal permeability, such as can be found in crystalline rocks, are recognised as desirable characteristics for a repository site.

Although groundwater in a regional flow system may go deeper than a local flow, this doesn't necessarily mean fewer open fractures are present (Chapter 4). So rapid flow is still possible in parts of large systems. Where a fault or major joint system provides a conduit for upward movement of groundwater, flow rates may also suddenly increase. It is still possible to say, however, that on average regional flow is very slow.

How slow is slow?

In hard rock with few faults and fractures, annual groundwater movements might be measured in centimetres a year, whereas in permeable sandstone, rates of centimetres or even metres a day are more appropriate. The problem is to calculate realistically what flow rates are in the field, since they are controlled by several interdependent features which vary significantly from one part of the system to another, particularly hydraulic conductivity and anisotropy.

The calculation that follows is very simplified, but it indicates the relative time scales of groundwater movement.

Suppose the repository was sited in fractured hard rock at a depth of 500 metres, and 200 metres or so from a near vertical fault through which groundwater was rising. If deep flow was roughly horizontal and moved no faster than half a metre a year, it would then take water circulating through the repository about 400 years to reach the fault. With a flow rate say ten times greater in the fault zone, groundwater could then rise 500 metres to the surface in another hundred years, thus completing its route from repository to biosphere in less than 500 years.

One of the many possible objections to relying on this sort of calculation is that even in a well-investigated site, the flow rate through the fractured zones is calculated from limited observation and may not represent an average over the whole zone — the flow may be significantly slower or faster in places. A second objection is that hydrogeological containment is only part of the story — but this is dealt with in succeeding Chapters.

Interactions

Different groundwater circulation systems can exist on different scales, in the same area, at the same time. Figure 5.6 shows how a local flow related to topography can co-exist with a regional flow moving in an opposing direction. The two flow systems may enhance or oppose each other. Where they are working in the same direction, flow could be increased. Where they work in opposite directions a zone of stagnant groundwater could, in theory, result from opposing forces cancelling each other out.

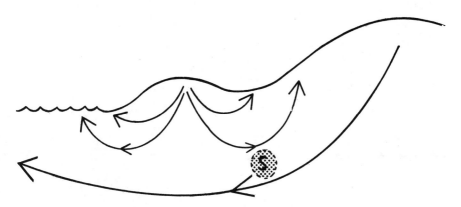

Figure 5.6 Contrasting flow directions in local and regional flow systems. S marks a stagnant zone.

On a large scale, flow seems more logical and predictable, because all sorts of local variations in permeability and anisotropy can be ignored and the geosphere can be treated as if it were rather uniform. The result is that although local flow may be important, and its interactions with regional flow significant, it is less studied. This is despite the fact that there may be circumstances where exceptions to large-scale averages are significant for radionuclide migration, and averaged predictions about groundwater circulation are inaccurate.

Summary

The concept of hydrogeological containment is an important aspect of the theory of geological containment of radioactive waste. Both the rate and scale of groundwater flow have a direct bearing on how long radionuclides can be isolated from the biosphere. Local and regional flow systems co-exist and are generally associated with the rapid and slow return respectively of groundwater and any dissolved or suspended solids to the biosphere. The boundary between salt and fresh groundwater at a coastal site could significantly alter flow paths and residence times.

Only detailed site investigation can provide information about flow systems at a particular site. Flow in hard fractured rock is generally slow but is difficult to calculate and predict. For any rock type, much reliance must be placed on statistical, computer-based experiments, because it is not possible to reproduce field conditions in a laboratory and long-term, large-scale real-world experiments cannot be done.

Even if groundwater carried radionuclides away from a repository, chemical reactions in the groundwater, as well as rock/water reactions, might retard the migration of radionuclides. Retardation is another essential feature of the theory of geological containment of radioactive waste and forms the subject of Chapter 6.

Chapter 6

Retardation

So far we've looked at how groundwater would influence radionuclide migration; the rocks themselves have only featured as inert frameworks for groundwater flow. But rocks are aggregates of minerals; minerals are naturally occurring chemical compounds; and where there are chemicals, there are chemical reactions, especially in the presence of water. The radioactive substances which would be released from a repository are also chemicals, and could react with groundwater and rock minerals in various ways.

Such chemical reactions could have two distinct results. They could *release* radionuclides to move through the geosphere (dissolved or suspended in groundwater) or they could *hold back* radionuclides and keep them deep underground, by preventing them from dissolving or by making them combine with the minerals in the rocks — and that's retardation.

In support of a single UK national repository, Nirex quotes reassuring statements such as 'typically, highly sorbed radionuclides move from one thousand to ten thousand times more slowly than the groundwater' (Saunders, 1988). If this can indeed be demonstrated to apply to a chosen repository site now and in the distant future, retardation would clearly contribute to successful geological containment. However, the problem in discussing retardation is that scientific knowledge of the retardation of radionuclide migration in the geosphere is not, so far, well-developed. The Parliamentary committee on Radioactive Waste Management commented in its 1988 report that 'work in...understanding [of retardation]...which is vital to the safety case [for a deep repository] is expected to continue for some years.'

Although a satisfactory understanding of retardation is still to be achieved, the basic idea is not hard to understand. If radionuclides are imagined as vehicles of all sorts of different shapes, sizes and capabilities, from tricycles to Porsches, retardation would be a bit like having underground police selectively pulling up some of the passing traffic, directing buses into special lanes and detaining other vehicles in parking places for spot checks. Some might never make it back onto the road, others might need replacement parts which were very hard to come by and others might be allowed to continue their journey when road conditions improved or minor repairs were done. There is no guarantee that each leg of the journey would be passable by all vehicles and in places the road might peter out altogether. Many roads lead to the biosphere eventually, but the way can be very long, very slow and very tortuous, so some vehicles are bound to decay before they get there.

To pursue the analogy, the Chemical Police are generally thought to have wide powers to direct and arrest passing vehicles, and it is their powers which are one of the main topics of this Chapter. First though, a little about suspension, dissolution and precipitation.

Suspended, Dissolved, Precipitated — a Whistle-Stop Tour

In the geosphere, radioactive substances can become part of solids such as mineral grains or crystals as a result of a chemical reaction. They can also become attached to the surface of mineral grains. Alternatively, they can be dissolved in water or associated with particles so tiny that they remain suspended in water. **Organic** compounds (chemicals containing the element carbon) derived from the decomposition of paper, cotton and wood in LLW, and from carbon-rich rocks such as some mudrocksand shales, can also form complex soluble chemicals to which long-lived radionuclides may become attached.

If radionuclides dissolve, or become attached to some other dissolved substance, they can migrate away from a repository in moving groundwater. If they are insoluble, or combined with or attached to another insoluble substance, they are likely to stay put while the water moves past. That is to say, there is retardation of radionuclide migration.

Clay minerals have a structure with spaces into which radionuclides can fit. Clay minerals which are part of the solid rock will also offer sites in which radionuclides can park; this means that a thick mudrock or shale might retard the passage of radionuclides by chemically 'sieving' them out.

On the other hand, clay minerals are tiny enough to get carried along by groundwater, taking with them any radioactive materials which may have become attached. However, if the water chemistry changes — for example, if it gets saltier (and normally, the deeper you go the saltier it gets) — the clay minerals may **flocculate**, that is, clump together to form heavier masses. These then settle out, leaving any circulating water to continue without them.

So it seems that on the one hand, clay minerals can detain radioactive nuclides, and on the other hand they may carry them along in suspension. To put it another way, clay minerals may be involved in *retardation* of radionuclide migration; they may also increase the ability of radioactive material to *migrate* away from a repository.

The behaviour of radionuclides in contact with organic molecules is still the subject of research (Hooker and Chapman, 1989) but it appears that they may become attached to organic molecules in the chemical conditions which are expected to develop in a repository after closure. Since the organic molecules themselves are dissolved in groundwater, transport of radionuclides away from a repository would be enhanced (Lever, 1989).

Colloids are minute particles which are found in most natural rock/water systems. They are sometimes composed of groups of particularly large organic molecules and are often associated with naturally occurring radionuclides. Colloids too may be important in transporting dissolved radionuclides from a waste disposal site, but more detailed studies are required before their contribution to repository safety can be properly assessed (Lever, 1989).

Some groundwater contains a lot of dissolved matter such as carbonate and silica, some of the components of other minerals dissolved from the rocks, and substances carried down in water from the surface. If the water gets overloaded with a particular kind of cargo, minerals will precipitate out: in other words solids begin to form, and attach themselves to the walls of pores or fractures.

Groundwater can give up some of its dissolved load (sometimes called TDS for Total Dissolved Solids) in another way as well. Some of the materials in the groundwater will swap places with materials in the rocks or soils which are in contact with the water. Each time substances are dissolved or precipitated, the chemistry of the groundwater is altered because something is added or subtracted. For this reason, hydrogeologists talk about the *evolution* of groundwater, since it undergoes both gradual and abrupt changes in character — changes which are often related to increasing or decreasing depth and increasing age of the water.

In the geosphere, temperature and pressure tend to increase with depth, so as groundwater circulates (and consequently moves vertically and laterally along gradients of temperature and pressure) it encounters different chemical conditions. Some of these may affect retardation of radionuclides.

It is possible to predict what may happen to groundwater chemistry in various circumstances. The problems arise in trying to predict the interactions of so many variables which could affect the behaviour of radionuclides, not just now but far into the future. For instance, the acidity of the groundwater, the amount of oxygen available and the geology of a site all vary considerably, and in addition, different radionuclides behave in different ways according to the conditions. Add to this the need to predict groundwater chemistry in the long-term future, then let all these variables interact in different combinations, and the task of repository geochemists begins to take on a complicated shape.

Solubility

Solubility refers to the ease with which substances dissolve. The **acidity** (and its opposite **alkalinity**) of groundwater is measured on the pH scale in which 7 represents neutral. A pH of less than 7 means an acid solution, more than 7 means alkaline. The degree of acidity can strongly affect whether substances (including radionuclides) dissolve in groundwater, that is, how soluble they are. Soluble radionuclides are able to migrate; in other words, pH affects the retardation of radionuclides.

Shallow groundwater, like rain, tends to be slightly acid; at the Altnabreac research site in Caithness, groundwater even near the bottom of a 300 metre deep borehole was found to be slightly acid (Kay and Bath, 1982). In general however, the older groundwater is, the more alkaline it is, due to progressive chemical reaction with the rocks.

Normally rainwater has an average pH of about 5.6, but for acid rain it can be much lower. Measurements of snow in the Cairngorm mountains in the Scottish Highlands in the last few years have recorded snow falls with a pH of 3 — about as acid as vinegar! Other snowfalls there have had a pH as high as 8 (comparable to that of baking soda) (Davies, 1989) Consequently the pH of percolating groundwater may vary quite widely. Microbes also have marked effects on the acidity of water and would certainly flourish in a repository. Their contribution will be examined in Chapter 7.

Solubility of Plutonium as a function of pH

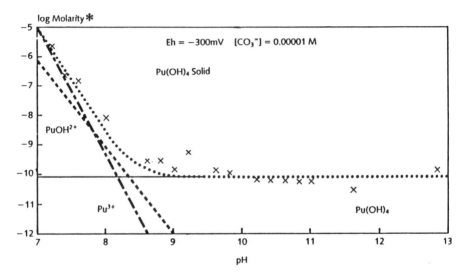

* log molarity is a measure of concentration

Figure 6.1 Control of plutonium solubility by pH.

The reactions of some radionuclides to changing pH have been studied. For instance plutonium is very soluble in acid water, but will remain mostly, though not entirely, insoluble as long as the pH is above about 8 (Figure 6.1). A number of other radionuclides are also very insoluble in alkaline conditions. This is the reason for plans to enclose buried waste in large quantities of concrete. Concrete is highly alkaline,so the theory is that even when it cracks and disintegrates in a repository, if there is enough of it around it will maintain an alkaline chemical environment which will retard the migration of radionuclides for about one million years (Saunders, 1987).

The solubility (and hence mobility) of radionuclides is also affected by how much oxygen is available. Uranium, for instance, is soluble in oxygen-rich (oxidising) conditions. This has long been known, but recent natural analogue studies of radionuclide mobility at a uranium mine in Brazil, and in peaty sediments close to a zone of uranium-rich sedimentary rock in Caithness, have provided detailed information (Hooker and Chapman, 1989).

When available oxygen has been used up by chemical reactions (including those caused by micro-organisms), conditions are referred to as reducing. Because different chemical reactions occur in reducing and oxidising conditions, the solubility of radionuclides can vary. For instance, it is thought that plutonium can be incorporated in dissolved organic substances in reducing conditions, and thus migrate easily in moving groundwater; and it is likely that reducing conditions would gradually become established in a sealed repository (Lever, 1989). In general, reducing conditions are characteristic of old, deep groundwater, while shallower groundwater normally contains plenty of oxygen. So in the end it is a combination of factors such as groundwater acidity and the availability of oxygen which help to determine the solubility, and hence retardation, of radionuclides in the geosphere.

Sorbtion

The chemical processes which affect how, and how far, radioactivity migrates in the geosphere also have much to do with

sorbtion. Sorbtion is a broad term which covers various types of transfer of materials between a solution (in this case groundwater) and the surfaces of a solid (pore walls, fracture walls, suspended solids) with which it is in contact. Even if radionuclides escape from a repository in moving groundwater, they may become attached to the solid rock, leaving the groundwater to go on without them. The concept of geological containment of radioactive waste relies strongly on sorbtion, so it is useful to take a look at the state of the art of sorbtion science.

Some radionuclides are strongly sorbing and others weakly sorbing. A strongly sorbing radionuclide will have a good chance of being contained in the geosphere (providing conditions are right) while a weakly sorbing radionuclide will tend to go along with the groundwater, unless its movement is arrested by combination with some other strongly sorbing substance. Uranium, thorium and plutonium are thought to be strongly sorbing, and iodine and neptunium weakly sorbing. Another long-lived radionuclide, technetium, is quoted by different authorities as either one or the other (Milnes, 1985; Bradbury and Jeffries, 1985). This is presumably because laboratory tests often give different values for sorbtion on the same rock type, depending on the experimental conditions and methods (Berry *et al*, 1987). Temperature, pressure and pH also affect solubility. In addition, the presence of organic substances and colloids can make predictions about sorbtion rather uncertain.

There are two ways in which our understanding of sorbtion can be improved. One is by actual observations of the geosphere, and the other is by experimental work in laboratories.

Field Observations — Natural Analogues

A small number of studies have been done (or are in progress) on concentrations of radioactive minerals in the environment, in-

Retardation

cluding those found in uranium mines and nuclear bomb testing sites. Where high concentrations of radionuclides occur naturally, their behaviour and distribution are analogous to the future behaviour and distribution of radionuclides artificially concentrated in a deep, underground repository. So these natural concentrations are labelled natural analogues, and are being intensively studied as models for repository behaviour and safety assessment. Since some of the natural analogues studied are many millions of years old, they provide clues as to what might happen in and around the repository over very long time scales.

The UK research programme is led by the UK Natural Analogue Co-ordinating Group (steered by the British Geological Survey) which submits an annual report to the Department of the Environment. The NACG's purpose is not only to improve understanding of processes which might operate in radioactive waste repositories, but to provide simple, easily understood examples of natural analogues which are designed to 'gain public acceptance of' and 'increase public confidence in' repositories (NACG, 1989). An example quoted in the Report as being a relevant and easily understood example of a natural analogue for geological containment is the excellent preservation of one million-year old wood in clay at a site in northern Italy. The inference we are invited to draw is presumably that the clay prevents change and decay from occurring. However, wood has little in common with radioactive waste, and this suggested analogue tells us nothing about the mobility of radionuclides in clay; it is irrelevant whether or not the structure of the wood (or the bulk of the LLW or ILW) is beautifully preserved.

The following natural analogue in particular has often been cited as proof that retardation works.

About eighteen hundred million years ago a large concentration of uranium formed at Oklo in Gabon, West Africa in a sequence

87

of sedimentary rocks. It was so large that it went critical: that is, there was a sufficient mass of uranium–235 to start chain reactions of the kind which produce the energy to generate electricity in a nuclear power station. The product was several tonnes of HLW concentrated in several adjacent natural reactor sites.

As far as is known, a good deal of the waste was contained within a ten metre zone around its points of origin. Among the radionuclides largely retained were plutonium, neptunium, indium, palladium, rhodium, yttrium, niobium and polonium. Those which were mainly lost by migration away from the site include caesium, iodine, cadmium, molybdenum, and the gases xenon and krypton. Lead showed variable migration, and local redistribution of uranium, barium, technetium, ruthenium, zirconium, strontium and rubidium seems to have occurred. The fate of tin, antimony, tellurium and americium was still unstudied in 1987 (Roxburgh, 1987).

It has been suggested that the evidence about the migration of reaction products at Oklo is equivocal: not enough is known about the changing chemical conditions over the last eighteen hundred million years for confident interpretation of the data collected; the chemical and physical conditions in which partial containment occurred are unclear. What *is* known, however, is that the chemistry of the Earth's atmosphere and shallow groundwater was radically different eighteen hundred million years ago from what it is today. Another possibility is that containment of some elements was not principally caused by sorbtion and insolubility but was a result of the protection afforded by the crystal structure of the uranium ore mineral, uraninite, which would not be present in a LLW/ILW repository (Roxburgh, 1987).

It is interesting to compare this sort of information — and speculation — about Oklo with other, reassuring statements.

'Detailed studies of the deposits [at Oklo] have shown that nearly all the heavy elements, including the plutonium and most of the fission products remained where they were formed.' (Saunders, 1987).

Studies at Oklo show that retardation has indeed occurred for some radionuclides. However not all the answers have been found, and little is known about exactly how and why retardation and migration of radionuclides occurred. Given the very different chemistry of the Earth's atmosphere and groundwater eighteen hundred million years ago, it is not clear whether a modern repository could be expected to behave in the same way. So while Oklo does provide a natural analogue for a radioactive waste repository, it doesn't prove — given our present state of knowledge — that a UK national repository at Sellafield or Dounreay or another possible site, would be safe.

Natural analogues of the movement of both radioactive and stable nuclides through clays and clay-rich rocks have also been studied. For instance, it has been shown that chloride movement through part of the London Clay amounts to only about 30 metres over the last ten to twenty thousand years (Nirex, 1988).

Clay minerals are excellent scavengers of **ions** in solution in the ways described earlier in this Chapter. In addition, since unfractured clays and clay-rich rocks such as mudrock and shale can be highly impermeable, they have always been thought likely to play a major part in retarding the movement of radionuclides.

However, recent work on diffusion in clay-rich rocks, done as part of the UK natural analogue study programme, casts doubt on this assumption (Cook, 1988). It appears that the very ability of clay minerals to attract radionuclides could produce a concentration leading to their rapid diffusion through the rock. In this way, significant transport of radionuclides might occur across impermeable clay or mudrock, which would be acting more like a sieve than a seal, with sorbtion *enabling* radionuclide transport, rather than causing retardation. Cook concludes that not enough is known about the physical state of undisturbed clays and shales to investigate the problem sensibly.

A problem with relying on natural analogues is that understanding fully how sorbtion, diffusion and transport of radionuclides in the geosphere actually works remains a long-term goal rather than an immediate practical possibility. This means that chemical retardation can be observed, but cannot be predicted with a high degree of confidence. It also means that the use of simple natural analogues, as a device to build public confidence in underground disposal of radioactive waste, is suspect.

The implications for prediction of repository safety can be explained by using another analogy. Observing and cataloguing retardation, but not understanding fully how and why it happens, is a bit like knowing that grass always starts to grow in the spring. You could then propose a theory that when the temperature reaches a certain level for a certain length of time, grass starts to grow. You could even do experiments which 'proved' that your theory was indeed correct. Successful farming (prediction of how the grass would grow) could be based on your theory. But one year you might find that the grass seeds remained obstinately dormant and your farm enterprise failed.

This would be the equivalent of predicting that sorbtion would occur and then finding it didn't. In terms of your theory of grass growth (or sorbtion) there is no explanation; your theory wouldn't allow you to consider that sometimes the expected event would fail to happen. Why couldn't you predict that the seeds would fail to grow? Because you didn't understand the exact conditions which made it happen — for instance that a particular combination of day length and temperature were critical for germination. Unfortunately in the case of a radioactive waste repository, it would be too late to prevent damage by the time you discovered the theory was inadequate. If the exact mechanisms of sorbtion remain unknown, any predictions about how much sorbtion of radionuclides will occur must be considered uncertain.

Laboratory Studies

Laboratory studies of sorbtion are also subject to uncertainty due to the impossibility of artificially re-creating realistic geosphere conditions. Depending on the experimental method and the exact mineral composition of the rock used, values derived for sorbtion of a particular radionuclide may vary widely, with one result anything from two to a hundred times greater than another (Bradbury and Jeffries, 1985; Lever, 1989).

Another kind of problem is that calculating rates of sorbtion of, say, a fractured granite or thick mudstone can be misleading. If the rock has low permeability, and most flow is concentrated in fracture zones associated with faulting, a completely different set of minerals may be found in the fractures from those in the main body of rock. These fracture minerals will have grown in circulating groundwater, and their solubilities and sorbtive properties may well be quite different from those of the host rock. So a lot must be known about the circulation system before calculations of the probable effects of sorbtion on the migration of radionuclides can be made.

Summary

An important aspect of the theory of geological containment of radioactive waste is retardation. Retardation means that radionuclides emerging from a repository along with circulating groundwater would not necessarily travel as far or as fast as the water which facilitated their escape. Both physical and chemical processes could retard their progress. But depending on the chemical conditions at any one time, some chemical processes could also make radionuclides more soluble and thus promote their migration away from the repository.

The processes involved in retardation are not well understood, so making accurate long-term predictions about transfer of radionuclides to the biosphere is difficult. It is clear, however, that we cannot assume that contaminated groundwater reaching the surface would contain the same amount or type of radionuclides it may have started off with underground.

The next Chapter focuses on two additional factors, gas generation and microbes in the biosphere, both of which could be vital elements in determining whether geological containment of radioactive waste works.

Chapter 7

Gases and Microbes

When deep disposal of ILW and LLW was first proposed for the UK, not much attention had been given to gas generation within the waste or to the activities of microbes in the geosphere. Research is now being done, but the level and quality of information about the behaviour of microbes in the geosphere does not yet match information about, for instance, groundwater circulation (Biddle *et al*, 1987).

In enclosed spaces, a build-up of gases can generate pressures high enough to damage or even destroy the container. The same principle applies if the space is a mined, underground repository and the container is rock, steel or concrete. On the other hand, venting gases to the surface to relieve the pressure means releasing radioactive gases to the biosphere.

Gases could have chemical as well as physical effects on containment of radioactive waste, since gases may dissolve in water and could alter groundwater chemistry.

Microbes too can radically change water chemistry and could even give a free ride to radionuclides sorbed onto them in circulating groundwater. Also, like all living things, microbes themselves produce gases, so we must add microbes and gases to the variables that might affect how radionuclides would behave in and around a deep repository.

Repository Gases And Their Sources

Although the waste itself would be the principal source of gas, *most* of the gas produced in a repository would not be radioactive.

Depending very much on the site in question, the geosphere could also make a contribution.

Within a repository itself, the principal gases are expected to be hydrogen, produced by the corrosion of steel drums, with carbon dioxide and methane arising from the breakdown of organic material in the waste by micro-organisms. LLW in particular contains large quantities of organic material such as wood, paper and cotton. Gas-producing micro-organisms would inevitably be present in them and could flourish and multiply in such an environment. It is expected that in a combined ILW/LLW store, each waste canister would produce, on average, its own volume of gas at atmospheric pressure each year (Nirex, 1988).

Of the radioactive gases, tritium, krypton–85, carbon–14 and radon–222 would all be released from stored waste, and they would be a potential hazard if they reached the surface.

The principal gas present from sources outside the repository would be methane, which can be released from the same organic-rich rocks (shales and mudrocks) which form convenient impermeable barriers to fluid movement in the geosphere. For instance, methane gas has been encountered in boreholes in the sedimentary rocks close to Sellafield.

Gas Accumulation and Dispersal

The significance of the non-radioactive gases generated in a repository lies mainly in their volume. Gas, like groundwater, is a fluid and therefore can flow in the geosphere. However, it differs from groundwater in some important ways; it is much more compressible, and it can dissolve in water at the high pressures of the geosphere, only to emerge from solution and increase in volume as pressures decrease.

Most people are familiar with compressed air and compressed

cooking gas in bottles. People who brew their own beer may also be familiar with the effects of too much compressed gas (produced by yeast microbes) in well-stoppered bottles. To put it in terms which might be used by the nuclear industry, the containment vessel ruptures suddenly. (Others might say the bottle exploded.)

The problem to be overcome in a repository is that if you seal it tightly to prevent radionuclides (such as the gases mentioned above) reaching the biosphere, you also seal in large volumes of hydrogen, carbon dioxide and so on. So you have a growing volume of gas in a fixed space. The more gas there is, the more it becomes compressed. The more gas is compressed, the greater the force it can exert on the walls of the containing rocks. If gas pressure exceeds the strength of the enclosing rock, something has to give, and that something could only be, first of all the steel and concrete containers, and secondly the rock surrounding the waste.

The uncertainty attached to the actual volumes of gas expected in a repository is well-illustrated in Figure 7.1 (Rees and Rodwell, 1988). The right hand line represents the slowest estimated rate of gas growth and the left hand line the fastest. Note that after about 60 years' corrosion, gases might amount to about one million cubic metres (minimum) or one thousand million cubic metres (maximum) at atmospheric pressure. With this degree of uncertainty it would not be prudent to put too much reliance on such estimates.

Unfortunately, the very rocks which might ensure slow, restricted, groundwater flow — fractured crystalline rocks — don't allow easy dispersal of gas. If the gas cannot disperse, the pressure will build up, and if the pressure is great enough, new fractures, or an extended system of fractures, could propagate through the rocks. Fractures which were previously closed might open and alter hydraulic conductivity. In other words, the

containment vessel might crack, and this in turn could significantly change groundwater flow patterns.

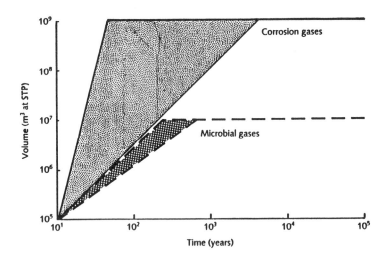

Figure 7.1 Gas generation from corrosion of steel in a
radioactive waste repository. All volumes calculated at
atmospheric pressure.

An alternative would be to deliberately *encourage* the dispersal of
gas towards the biosphere — but this brings us back to the
problem of releasing radioactive gases as well. Other solutions,
as yet untested, could include reducing gas production by at-
tempting to engineer an environment in which degradation of
steel, concrete and organic wastes by microbes (or by their by-
products such as sulphuric acid) would be limited. Whether a
suitably engineered repository could provide a sufficiently long-
term solution is another question.

Microbes

The diversity of micro-organisms and their ability to survive in 'impossible' conditions is astonishing (Christophi *et al*, 1983). As well as producing large amounts of gas, microbes in a repository could cause steel corrosion, degradation of cement and significant changes in groundwater acidity. Some microbes produce hydrogen sulphide gas and corrosive acids which can damage cement and concrete. A well-documented consequence of their activity was an explosion at a landfill site in Edinburgh in 1982, when fireworks, encased in concrete that was thought to be virtually indestructible, blew up (Godfrey, 1989). Different groups of microbes can thrive in reducing and oxidising conditions, in environments where organic material is scarce as well as where it is plentiful, at very high temperatures and pressures and at a high level of radioactivity.

One of the factors which limits the ability of microbes to grow and multiply in the geosphere is the availability of carbon. Carbon is essential for life but many igneous and metamorphic rocks have little or no carbon in them. However, carbon might actually be incorporated into a repository as a consequence of other considerations in the design, as at Forsmark in Sweden. The floor of the repository at Forsmark has been thickly lined with montmorillonite, a type of clay. There are two reasons for this: first, clays have a high rate of sorbtion, and second, this particular clay is also good at absorbing water (including radioactive water). Montmorillonite is known as a 'swelling clay' because its structure allows it to increase its volume as it absorbs water. The idea is that the clay will soak up leaked radionuclides along with the water, radionuclides will be sorbed on to clay mineral surfaces and at the same time block up small fractures in the floor of the repository as it swells.

However, montmorillonite also contains carbon, and could therefore encourage the growth of some kinds of gas-producing, canister-corroding, concrete-destroying microbes. So there may be disadvantages as well as benefits involved in this method of improving containment. Radionuclide mobility could also be increased by sorbtion, both by means of enhanced diffusion and by micro-organisms which can themselves move around in circulating groundwater.

Summary

Gases, both radioactive and non-radioactive, would be generated in a waste repository in a variety of ways. The problem to be solved is how to prevent high gas pressures fracturing surrounding rock and altering groundwater flow paths without at the same time releasing hazardous gases to the biosphere.

The more favourable a repository site is from a hydrogeological point of view, the more problems it poses for gas evolution and migration. Low permeability rocks are favoured for a repository because they would probably allow very little, very slow groundwater circulation. However, gases would probably not be able to migrate easily through such rocks. The risk is that very high gas pressures would build up finally causing the gas to escape by forcing open previously closed fractures and altering groundwater flow.

If gas and microbes begin to look a bit like the enemy within, it is also necessary in repository planning and design to look at the enemy without and assess defences. With this in mind, the next Chapter examines how a repository could withstand large-scale changes in the natural environment.

Chapter 8

Earthquakes and Climatic Change

Long-lived radionuclides require equally long-term containment. So far, we have looked at causes of, and constraints on, containment associated with the repository itself. But three major types of external natural event could seriously affect geological containment of radionuclides. These are earthquakes, climatic warming (the greenhouse effect) and glaciation.

Earthquakes

Earthquakes occur when accumulated stress along fault planes is suddenly relieved as the blocks of the Earth's crust on either side move past each other.

The destruction caused by an earthquake is related to two factors — the depth of the focus, which is where the movement occurs and the energy is released, and what and who is around to be damaged. The amount of energy released is measured on the **Richter scale** which rises from 1 to 10. Each unit represents an energy nearly 30 times greater than the one below. So point 4 represents a thirty times greater release of energy than point 3 and about 1,000 times greater (i.e. 30 x 30) than point 2. The terrible 1988 Armenian earthquake was measured at about 6.8 on the Richter scale, whilst the earthquake near San Francisco in 1989 measured 6.9, causing extensive destruction, though with much smaller loss of life than the Armenian event.

Figure 8.1 The historical record of earthquakes in the UK. The smallest dots represent a magnitude of 3, and the largest 5–6 on the Richter scale

Although they are nowhere near as destructive as the Armenian and San Francisco events, earthquakes do occur in the UK (Figure 8.1). In 1979, a magnitude 4.8 earthquake occurred near Carlisle. Chimneys and roof tiles were brought down in an area of 200,000 square kilometres and over 90 aftershocks, some exceeding magnitude 4.0, were detected over the next two years (Turbitt, 1986). In July 1984 an earthquake of magnitude 5.1 occurred about 20 kilometres beneath the Lleyn peninsula in North Wales and almost 400 aftershocks have been detected.

Some recent earthquakes in the UK include a group which occurred in the west of Scotland in 1985 and 1986. The locations and magnitudes were as follows: Oban 4.2, Faslane (the nuclear naval base on the Clyde near Glasgow) 3.5, Mallaig 3.7 and Loch Nevis 3.0. Tremors are frequently recorded from the Great Glen fault zone which contains Loch Ness and divides the Scottish Highlands from coast to coast. However, daily commuters across the fault don't feel a thing, though the suspension bridge linking Inverness with the rock on the other side of the fault is built to withstand a moderate earthquake just in case.

The risk of earthquake damage has been assessed not only by the nulcear industry but also by the oil exploration industry in the North Sea. Defining areas where the probable energy and frequency of earthquakes is likely to be significant is called seismic hazard mapping. One recent seismic hazard map (Woo and Muir Wood 1986) shows the north and east of Scotland and north east England (as far south as Bridlington) as an aseismic zone – a zone where earthquakes don't occur.

However, earthquakes can and do occur in these areas; for example, the 1927 Thurso earthquake, when many people were woken up during the night as furniture and crockery was shaken; and there are some intriguing tales whose origin could lie in Earth tremors.

For example, a former quarryman, Archie Sinclair, well-known for his interest in fossil fish from the sedimentary rock sequence known as the Old Red Sandstone, relates how in that beautiful part of Caithness which advertises itself as 'miles from nowhere' and is certainly devoid of railway lines, he and his cousin heard a noise of increasing volume which 'resembled a steam engine labouring under great pressure' (Sinclair, 1988). As this was 1925, it was certainly not a low-flying jet fighter either. Quite suddenly the noise came to an end. But on a fine day fourteen years later, in the same spot, just over the crest of a low hill, Mr. Sinclair passed through a narrow zone where the air temperature was several degrees higher than the surroundings. He turned back to verify this unusual observation. It is just possible — though quite unproven — that gas was escaping from the geosphere, accompanied by a minor Earth tremor and realignment or opening of fractures. Gas is often associated with oil-bearing rocks, and oil companies have recently been granted licences to search for oil and gas in the sedimentary basin of which Caithness forms a part. So perhaps such speculation is not all that far-fetched. However, the real point of this tale is the unpredictability of Earth tremors.

In high latitudes, including northern Britain, the thick sheet of ice which formed during the last Ice Age made the underlying Earth's crust sink under its great weight. The stresses created by the crust's slow return to its former level after the ice melted may be responsible for some earthquakes in unexpected places. Although the last of the ice disappeared thousands of years ago, some parts of Sweden which were depressed by as much as 800 metres are still rising at the rate of about 1 centimetre a year. Britain was covered by a smaller icesheet; the readjustment was less and is more or less completed now.

Since 1980, a detailed British Earthquake Archive has been compiled on behalf of the Electricity Generating Boards and

British Nuclear Fuels plc. for use in choosing sites for new nuclear installations, while the oil industry has gained useful information about earthquakes beneath the North Sea from studies by the British Geological Survey. In addition, there is both a UK network and a world-wide network of earthquake recording stations. These networks monitor earthquakes, which produce vibrations (called seismic waves) which reverberate through the body of the Earth. So earthquakes are well-documented, including very many tremors which are simply too small to affect everyday activities but can be detected by sensitive instruments.

The recording of earthquakes causes few problems; the science of earthquake prediction on the other hand is anything but cut and dried. Earthquakes occur at generally unpredictable intervals. Although there is no dispute about the existence of well-defined areas where earthquakes are very likely to occur (called **seismic zones**), they also occur from time to time in unexpected places.

As we have seen, earthquakes with magnitudes exceeding 3 or 4 do occur in areas of the west coast of Scotland, around Anglesey and in Cumbria (Turbitt, 1986), although no part of Britain is considered to be within a seismic zone. According to Nirex, all these areas have suitable geology for a radioactive waste repository.

If an earthquake focus is deep, say 100 kilometres, a good deal of the energy of even a large earthquake will have dissipated by the time the seismic waves arrive within a few hundred metres of the surface. A much smaller earthquake occurring only 10 kilometres down could be more destructive. However, risk analysis suggests that no tremors are likely to occur anywhere in Britain on a scale which could damage a well-engineered structure (Woo, 1986).

Although an earthquake in Britain seems unlikely to cause significant damage to a repository, the relatively young science of earthquake prediction has thrown up some lines of investigation which could be significant for hydrogeological waste containment. Radon and helium gas seepage, as well as rises and falls in water levels in wells and boreholes, precede some earthquakes. These effects must indicate altered sub-surface fluid circulation and seem likely to be caused by the opening of previously closed fractures and fissures.

Fractures may also be realigned as stresses build up in the rocks before an earthquake. If the stresses are different from what they were before, fluid circulation patterns may change. If circulation patterns change, hydrogeological containment would not operate in the way predicted and might no longer correspond to a set of conditions previously considered essential for long-term safety.

Insignificant tremors do not cause surface damage. They may be too low energy for anything but a sensitive seismometer to notice, or nothing that a well-engineered structure can't cope with. They may have no significant effect on hydraulic conductivity and underground fluid circulation patterns around a potential repository site — but systematic investigation of such effects remains to be done.

Global Warming — the Greenhouse Effect

When we burn fossil fuels such as oil, gas, coal and petrol, we release carbon dioxide into the atmosphere. Now carbon dioxide is particularly effective at trapping some of the Earth's heat which would otherwise be transmitted back into space as infrared radiation. So it seems probable that the growing proportion of carbon dioxide in the atmosphere, resulting from our use of fossil fuels, is the cause of a small but definite rise in global temperature which has been observed over the last few decades. This global warming process is often called the 'greenhouse effect'.

'Greenhouse effect' is a rather misleading term, however, since global warming is likely to produce very varied effects in different climatic and geographic zones. The Sahara might well become hotter and drier, but Britain could become wetter, and other areas at similar latitudes perhaps suffer a more extreme kind of climate with warmer summers but colder winters.

There are many uncertainties in the enormously complicated calculations which have to be made. Most researchers currently seem to agree on a global average temperature rise of between 2°C and 5°C over the next few decades. The effects on the ecology of our planet could be immense, but the significance for geological containment of radioactive waste lies in the consequences for hydrogeology.

If the world's climate continues to warm, the sea will also warm. When water warms up it expands. If the water container (in this case the ocean basins) remains the same size, the seawater will come further up the sides; in other words it will flood low-lying coastal ground. Vast amounts of additional water would flood into ocean basins too, because of melting of the Antarctic and Greenland ice sheets and of glaciers, which contain most of the world's fresh water.

Some estimates suggest an average sea level rise of one or two metres over the next century. This may not seem dramatic, and it is small compared to rises of up to 120 metres which have occurred in the geological past. But even a small rise could be catastrophic for many densely populated coastal areas throughout the world. In the context of our topic, most of the areas of the UK mainland designated as having potential for radioactive waste containment would be affected. Patterns of coastal erosion and sediment transport could be altered, river courses changed, boundaries between fresh and salt groundwater affected. Formerly secure buildings or construction sites might be regularly exposed to the kind of destructive storms and floods which used to be expected only once in fifty or a hundred years. Each of these events could introduce unknowns into carefully constructed models of how containment would continue to operate over the next few decades and indeed centuries.

If Britain became wetter as well as warmer, local groundwater circulation patterns could be changed because more precipitation means more percolation and possibly more vigorous, deeper flow. Groundwater chemistry would also be affected.

Attempts to predict what would happen in the future can be based on our knowledge of what has happened in the past. The repeated warming and cooling of the climate in the last two million years has left many traces in sediments and polar ice, and is recorded by landforms such as submerged forests and raised beaches, and by fossil plant and animal remains. However, just what the greenhouse effect will do to our climate in the next few decades is very uncertain — and predictions about changes in hydrogeology and their effect on radioactive waste containment are not easy to make.

Nirex recognises that the greenhouse effect introduces major uncertainties into models of repository safety. The time-scale of expected change is short, and substantial effects could be felt within a matter of decades.

Ice Ages

Over the last two million years there have been numerous major glaciations when most of Britain was covered by ice sheets or glaciers and the south of the country had a sub-Arctic climate. Sandwiched between glaciations were interglacial periods like the one we are enjoying today, when the ice sheets retreated to polar latitudes and glaciers receded to the high mountains in areas with a continental climate.

Less dramatic changes in climate are also common. Many of our 'traditional' Christmas card scenes are derived from the 'Little Ice Age' of the 17th and 18th centuries when the River Thames froze over every winter and people skated and built bonfires on the ice. Over seven thousand years ago, when neolithic people lived in what we now call the village of Skara Brae in the Orkney islands (today windswept and almost treeless), the climate was mild enough for deer and other mammals to roam in birch and hazel woods.

These were not the statistically insignificant series of mild winters or hot summers which most of us can recall from our own experience, but real, longer-term shifts in climate. And statistically speaking, we are due for another Ice Age within the next blink of a geological eyelid (perhaps within the next ten thousand years) if the average interval between recent ones is any guide. The contrary effect of climatic warming on these predictions is unknown.

Timescales of climatic change over thousands or tens of thousands of years are comparable with the half-lives of some radionuclides, and much shorter than others, so it is pertinent to ask what the effects of glaciation could be on a repository.

Active glaciers and ice sheets erode the land, carving away and smoothing the surface rocks to a depth of 200 metres or more, transporting debris for tens (or even hundreds) of kilometres and sometimes plastering great thicknesses of drift on the ground beneath. Ice has moulded the landscape of most of modern Britain like a gigantic sculptor, but it affects relative sea and land levels as well.

Obviously ice sheets and glaciers are composed of frozen water. But perhaps less obviously, as they grow, they extract water from the finite supply available — which is mainly the seas. The greater the volume of ice on land, the more sea-level falls. Rises and falls of tens of metres are well-documented consequences of past glaciations. A sea level fall of 70 metres would mean that you could walk from the east coast of England right across the North Sea to Denmark or directly south-west from Sellafield to Anglesey or from Skye to County Antrim.

Such radical changes in the relative level of land and sea mean that in times of major climatic change coastlines are impermanent features. Hence a coastal radioactive waste repository entrance needs to be protected from rises in sea level. Even if a repository were protected from submergence in the sea, groundwater circulation would be modified by erosion of up to 200 metres of rock above it, by uplift after the melting of an ice sheet, and by deposition of up to 100 metres of sediments on the ground above.

Summary

It is very unlikely that earthquakes pose a direct hazard to a suitably sited and engineered deep waste store in Britain, but small, non-destructive tremors might affect fluid circulation in the vicinity of a repository.

The observed global warming, if it continues, will produce climatic changes and associated sea-level changes. These may affect groundwater circulation and the integrity of a repository in a matter of decades if actual amounts of percolating groundwater differ from those predicted during repository design. It introduces a significant uncertainty into safety assessments.

Among the effects of glaciation are deep erosion, changes in water flow and sediment deposition, altered drainage patterns, deeply frozen ground, emergence of large areas of land at present under the sea and changes in the position of coastlines. Consequently, altered groundwater circulation patterns are inevitable and predicting them with any degree of confidence is a matter of great difficulty.

Computer models of how groundwater circulation would alter in periods of drought or higher rainfall can be constructed. The difficulty is to know if the data fed into the computer are realistic. Chapter 11 takes a closer look at models of this kind.

Up to this point we have been looking at different aspects of the concept of geological containment of radioactive waste. It is time now to get down to practicalities and examine how decisions about site selection can be made. That is the subject of the next Chapter.

Chapter 9

UK Repository Sites and Their Geology

It is clear that geological criteria for selecting repository sites must aim to maximise retardation and to minimise both radionuclide migration and subsequent escape to the biosphere. With this in mind, we can list conditions likely to favour containment, and then use this list to define suitable geological environments.

Appropriate Geology

For containment to operate, the following conditions seem desirable:

- slow groundwater circulation with long groundwater circulation paths, or restricted or stagnant groundwater circulation.

- low permeability rock.

- rock likely to favour sorbtion.

- chemical conditions favourable to precipitation of radioactive materials.

- seismic stability.

- flat topography.

- geologically simple structures.

- absence of major faults and fracture zones.

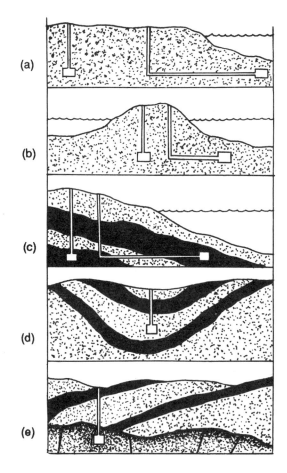

Figure 9.1 Suitable geological environments for an underground radioactive waste repository, according to Nirex. (a) Hard rock, low relief, under land or sea. (b) Small island. (c) Seaward-dipping sedimentary rocks. (d) Inland sedimentary rock basin. (e) Basement under sedimentary cover (BUSC).

Other conditions which would be necessary to satisfy safety requirements for a deep disposal site include:

- sufficient fracturing to allow gas escape

- thick, laterally extensive rock masses

- mechanical stability of the host rock

- sufficient depth of burial to avoid glacial erosion

- protection from changes in groundwater circulation associated with climatic change or Earth tremors

- absence of extractive operations (water, petroleum, mining, quarrying)

Site Selection

Following criteria of this kind, some general types of geological environment were defined for Nirex by the British Geological Survey as potentially suitable for a repository (Figure 9.1).

The next step was to produce a map of the UK, showing in broad terms where these environments might be found (Figure 9.2). Computer models of predicted radionuclide migration were used to rank different types of geological environment according to the amount of protection from radiation they might offer over the next ten thousand years and beyond.

A number of repository designs were considered:

- land-based, including coastal and small island sites

- under the seabed but accessed from land

- off-shore

By 1989 Nirex had decided that the best option was a coastal or inland repository in basement under sedimentary cover (BUSC). Hard rock locations in low relief terrain were thought to provide

Figure 9.2 Potential areas for siting an underground radioactive waste repository in the UK, as defined in 1989 by Nirex. Compare this with the areas defined in 1987 shown in Figure 1.2

inferior long-term radiological protection. Note that radiological protection does not necessarily mean the same as geological containment; the purpose of radiological protection is to minimise the radiation dose to members of the public, and this may involve the dilution of radionuclides in the sea. The ability of the sea to dilute and disperse radionuclides seems to have been important in Nirex's preference for coastal sites overlain by seaward-dipping sediments.

Uninhabited islands were considered to pose problems for transport of both waste and construction materials, and of facilities for workers.

An off-shore site was also considered. It lay beneath sixty metres of water in metamorphic and igneous rock off the west coast of Scotland. This is probably the Hebrides platform, which lies immediately to the west of the Western Isles. Nirex believes that off-shore disposal in crystalline rock would give the best radiological protection of all, but decided that the advantages of having the sea to dilute any leaks of radioactive material were offset by the dangers of working off-shore.

Finally, many non-geological criteria further reduced the range of possibilities before two BUSC sites, Sellafield and Dounreay, were chosen. All these selection procedures are fully described in Nirex Report No. 71 (1989). Both of the chosen sites already had a commitment to the nuclear industry and in each case a limited amount of site-specific geological information was already available.

However, only limited information was available about the hydrogeology and indeed about the actual hard rock in which a repository might be constructed. At each of the sites, the presence of the hard rock at depth was inferred, not proved; its exact depth was unknown; its chemical and mechanical properties were uncertain; and an educated guess was that it was moderately fractured and cut by some small and some very large faults. Further details of site geology are given in later sections of this Chapter.

Detailed Site Investigation

Once the sites were named, Nirex's next task was to plan 'detailed site investigation'. The sketchy details of site geology needed to be filled in, but basic research work on the concept of geological containment was also far from complete. Much remained to be learned about, among other things, fluid movement through fracture systems in hard rock, the diffusion of radionuclides through clay-rich rocks, the effects of climatic warming on the hydrogeology, the role of micro-organisms in influencing ground-water chemistry, the behaviour of some radionuclides in a variety of chemical environments, the generation and behaviour of gas in and around a repository and the validity of predictions relating to the medium- to long-term future.

So a more accurate description of the stage of development designated 'detailed site investigation' might be 'detailed research'. Three different kinds of research are involved:

- a detailed investigation of the geological structures, geo-chemistry, hydrogeology and rock mechanics of a site and its surrounding area.

- Basic research applicable to a particular site, such as sorbtion or fluid flow in a particular kind of fractured hard rock.

- the development of adequate computer models.

Computer models are required to predict the future behaviour of radionuclides in a variety of circumstances and to fill in the gaps — that is, the large zones of the geosphere inaccessible to direct observation.

This kind of 'site investigation' could last up to ten years. It is different in nature from the site investigations routinely carried out for all major construction work. In such cases the purpose is to apply a series of well-established tests and technologies in order to produce standard sets of information. Site investigation for a radioactive waste repository means testing a number of theories whose scientific basis is incomplete. Not only has basic research still to be done, but there is little past experience to tell us where things might go wrong: geological disposal of radioactive waste, unlike mining or water exploration, is something new and virtually untried. So the use of the phrase 'site investigation' to describe the work at Dounreay and Sellafield may be misleading.

'Site investigation' implies the project will go ahead once standard data have been acquired; 'site research' or 'field research' imply uncertainty about the outcome, but are perhaps more appropriate terms.

The nature of this problem is noted in the International Atomic Energy Agency's 1977 report on the selection of sites for radioactive waste disposal:

'The extreme complexity of many geological environments and of the rock features that govern the presence and circulation of groundwater does not make it feasible to derive strict criteria for the selection of a site for a radioactive waste repository in a geological formation. Each potential repository location must be evaluated according to its own unique geological and hydrogeological setting.' (IAEA, 1977).

At the beginning of the 1980s the results of geological research at all the UK nuclear sites were published by the Institute of Geological Sciences, now renamed the British Geological Survey (BGS) (Robins, 1980). The work was carried out for the Department of the Environment and the aim was to establish the suitability of the sites for deep disposal of LLW and ILW. Results of this work at Sellafield and Dounreay are summarised below, together with more recent information.

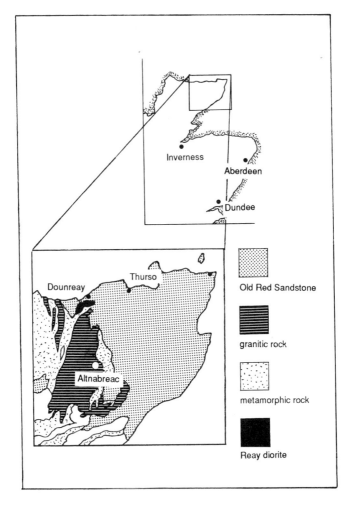

Figure 9.3 Simplified geological sketch map of the Dounreay area, Caithness.

Dounreay

Category of site: coastal, with seaward dipping sediments overlying hard, fractured rock (also known as BUSC — basement under sedimentary cover).

Underneath patchy, thin, superficial deposits at Dounreay are a group of sedimentary rocks belonging to the series of rocks known as the Old Red Sandstone. These consist of strata made up of sandstones, siltstones and mudstones, with the beds varying in thickness from a few centimetres to a few metres. Thin limestones also occur in places and at the base of the sequence are conglomerates and other coarse-grained rocks. This information is generalised from overall knowledge of the area since no deep boreholes on site have yet been sunk (December 1989).

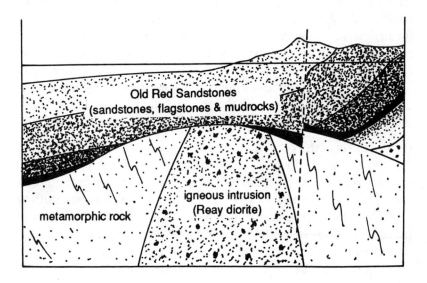

Figure 9.4 A prediction of the geology at Dounreay, Caithness, according to Nirex.

An unconformity separates these sedimentary rocks from the much older metamorphic schists on whose weathered upper surface they were deposited. A large igneous intrusion was believed to underlie this site at about 350 metres below the surface (Figure 9.4).

For the 1980 IGS study of Dounreay, twenty exploratory bore-holes were drilled to depths of up to 80 metres to clarify the nature of the geological succession. The educated guess in 1980 was that about 325 metres thickness of Old Red Sandstone underlay the site. The extent of the intrusive rock and the nature of its contact with the country rock (vertical? low angle? associated with substantial fracturing?) remained uncertain.

The IGS 1980 survey concluded that 'the potential for radioactive waste disposal within the Old Red Sandstone is poor' — since fairly rapid groundwater movement associated with extensive fissure permeability was likely. The report further concluded: 'A repository within these strata could, however, be envisaged in the expectation that leachate flowing through the formation will eventually discharge into the sea.' (Leachate is groundwater containing dissolved material.) No detailed information about local and regional groundwater flow backs up this proposal.

On the basis of the general principle that groundwater flow would be reduced in hard rock, the report pointed to the deeply buried metamorphic and intrusive rocks as having greater potential for radioactive waste disposal — including high level, heat-emitting waste — despite the fact that a likelihood of substantial fissure permeability has been shown by other studies. In other words, the best guess was that if water-containing fractures could be avoided, containment in the hard rock would be more effective.

These conclusions were *not* based on detailed knowledge of local and regional groundwater flow,recharge and discharge, ground-water chemistry, the effects of a boundary between salt water and fresh water on groundwater travel paths and return times to the surface, sorbtion effects or structural relations between the rock types. However they form a basis for defining further research needs.

To improve on existing knowledge about the deep geological structures (and the presumed presence at depth of crystalline rocks) at the site, geophysical surveys were done for Nirex, but 'did not confirm the deep structures' (Nirex, 1989). However a seismic survey done in December 1988 has been interpreted to show no Reay Diorite beneath the site and about 500 metres of sedimentary rock directly overlying the Moine metasediments (Figure 5), making Nirex's 1989 published prediction of the geology (Figure 9.4) inaccurate. A large intrusive igneous body was however found at a depth of over 2,000 metres.

Among the geological questions to be answered at Dounreay are:

• the effects of faulting on hydrogeology.

• the effects of a boundary beneath the coast between salt water and fresh water on groundwater circulation pathways and residence times in present and future climatic conditions.

• the amount of sorbtion possible in a sedimentary sequence dominated by fissure permeability.

• the chemical and mechanical properties of the basement rock in which a repository would be built.

These, and many other questions, would have to be answered before waste containment at Dounreay could be pronounced satisfactory.

Despite the absence of this kind of detailed information, Nirex has sugggested that for the first ten thousand years of the life of a repository at Dounreay, 'radionuclides migrating in groundwater would emerge into a marine biosphere' (Nirex, 1989). In other words, radionuclides would eventually leak into the sea. However, if sea level fell during an Ice Age, much of the radioactive groundwater discharge would then be on land, under ice; though it hardly seems necesssary to rely on sophisticated computer models to reach this obvious conclusion. Nirex's 1989 Report makes no comment on what would happen to migrating radionuclides if the sea level were to rise in the next few decades because of climatic warming.

Sellafield (formerly known as Windscale)

Category of site: coastal; basement under seaward dipping sediments (BUSC).

Sellafield lies in a gently sloping coastal area, crossed by rivers draining from the rugged topography of the Lake District. Superficial deposits of river and glacial sediments overlie the thick St. Bees Sandstone which also contains conglomerates, shales and evaporites at its base. As at Dounreay, the sedimentary rocks dip seawards on the margin of a thick sedimentary basin.

Taking into account the angle at which the bedding planes dip (that is, the angle at which they are inclined), it seems likely that there are about 900 metres of sedimentary rock beneath the Sellafield complex. Most of the rock is sandstone with a very poor potential for sorbtion, and with permeability which varies from low to high in different zones, so that fractures are likely to provide the route for a significant amount of groundwater flow.

Robins (1980) states that highest permeability values in nearby areas were found during pumping tests in boreholes adjacent to a fault. Without providing supporting evidence, the report adds that high fissure permeability is only expected in the upper few hundred metres. Groundwater flow is from the high land in the east towards the west and the sea.

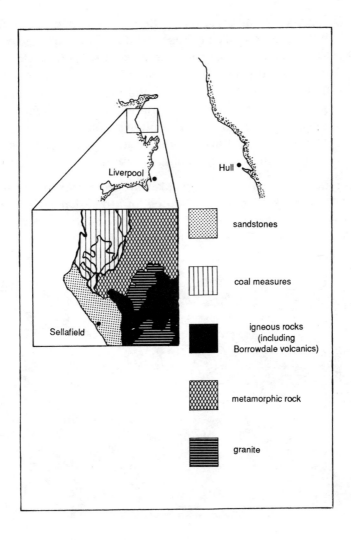

Figure 9.5 Simplified geological sketch map of the Sellafield area, Cumbria.

Robins specifically eliminated Sellafield from consideration for a LLW/ILW deep repository because it did not meet the geological criteria for waste disposal. 'The sandstone is not suitable for solid radioactive waste disposal because of its moderate, but variable, permeability.' The report adds 'Shaft sinking is extremely difficult in this formation because of the ingress of groundwater...the sandstone is too clean for much sorbtion of radionuclides to take place... However, repository design could be envisaged whereby any leachate is allowed to...discharge into the Irish Sea'.

In summary, the gist of the report is that geological containment at Sellafield is likely to be very limited, but the escape of radionuclides could be delayed by their passage through the permeable St. Bees Sandstone, after which they would be dispersed in the Irish Sea.

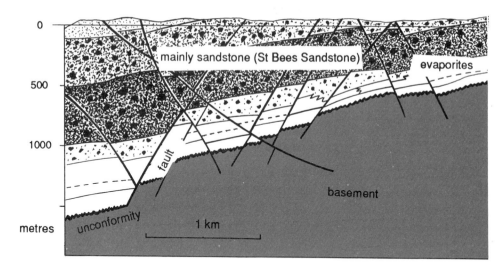

Figure 9.6 Predicted cross-section through the upper part of the geosphere running NE from the Sellafield nuclear site.

Ten years later, Sellafield is one of only two sites in Britain of special interest for waste disposal and the options have widened to include the basement volcanic rocks (Figure 9.6). Immediately beneath Sellafield, the upper surface of the Borrowdale Volcanics is now put at about 1,000 metres below the ground surface, stretching to the limit the 1,000 metres depth proposed as a maximum for a repository.

However, two or three kilometres inland from Sellafield, the volcanics rise to within 500 metres of the surface, suggesting the possibility of an inland site accessed by a long tunnel from the Sellafield works. Nirex has stated a preference for this option with a repository at a minimum depth of 550 metres and 'reception facilities on the Sellafield works site' (Nirex, 1989).

As at Dounreay, Nirex predicts that any radionuclide leakage in the first ten thousand years would be into the sea. Geological features of the site which support this prediction include the fact that regional groundwater flow is towards the sea through the seaward-dipping sediments. In addition, impermeable mudrocks and evaporites probably overlie the Borrowdale volcanics (Figure 9.6) and could in theory prevent groundwater taking a short route to the surface. However, other features introduce major uncertainties into calculations of groundwater flow paths and residence times at Sellafield. They are: first, the presence of numerous large faults cutting sediments and basement alike and increasing the possiblity of rapid vertical flow; and second, the character of the basement rocks is little known, but it is thought to be well-fractured.

In addition, future radiation doses have been calculated on the basis that '70% of the groundwater return time is spent in the low permeability barrier provided by the postulated layer of anhydrite and shales which overlie the basement downstream of the repository location' (Nirex, 1989). Given that available geological information is scanty, and that these calculations depend on a 'postulated' layer of anhydrite and shales (which may be cut or displaced by faults), the accuracy of dose calculations seems questionable. (**Anhydrite** is a calcium sulphate mineral with no water in its structure.)

However, on general principles it is possible to argue that ground-water is unlikely to percolate from 'well-fractured' (and therefore permeable) basement into less permeable shales and evaporites, since the water will take the path of least resistance. Groundwater flow would therefore be concentrated in fractures and the majority of open fractures are likely to be vertical rather than horizontal. Since Figure 9.6 shows numerous major faults linking basement, sediments and the land surface (and by implication, the sea-bed), there may be routes to the surface for migrating radionuclides which short-circuit the long, seaward-dipping pathway envisaged by Nirex. If this is so, calculated radiation doses and return times to the biosphere calculated by Nirex could be highly inaccurate.

At both Sellafield and Dounreay, heat from high activity ILW is expected to raise temperatures to around 80°C after repository closure (Nirex, 1989). This is quite high enough to cause any hydrated clay minerals to lose a lot of their water, as well as adding water vapour to the other repository gases and providing in-creased energy for groundwater circulation through and around a repository. Where water circulation is slow and difficult, the result could be high pressures and additional stresses on the rock. Where circulation is relatively easy, the result could be unpredictable perturbations in the flow system.

In announcing the choice of Sellafield and Dounreay for detailed investigation, Nirex confirmed the possibility that another, as yet secret, site on a short list of four would have to be studied if Sellafield and Dounreay proved unsuitable. So, for the record, a comparable summary of the geology of two more sites, which may well have been considered, are included. They differ from the other two in several important respects; Altnabreac in Caithness is inland, as opposed to coastal; it is not the site of an existing nuclear installation; and no sedimentary rocks are involved. In contrast, the potential site at Billingham in Cleveland is a worked-out anhydrite mine.

Altnabreac

Category of site: inland; hard rock with low relief.

An extensive research programme into HLW disposal was started in 1978 at a number of UK sites including Altnabreac. The work was sub-contracted to the IGS by the UKAEA. It resulted in numerous detailed reports into the structure, hydrogeology, geochemistry, rock mechanics and geomicrobiology of the Altnabreac area. Three deep boreholes were drilled to 300 metres and twenty four shallow ones to about 40 metres.

At Altnabreac, peat and glacial deposits overlie hard rock which is weathered to a depth of about 40 metres by slightly acid surface waters. The rock is metamorphic and intruded by the Strath Halladale Granite which is 3–5 kilometres thick and is itself partially metamorphosed. Of course, when a large body of granite intrudes into cold, country rock, great forces are involved; at Altnabreac this is reflected in complex faulting and fractures filled with a variety of often reactive minerals which differ from those forming the main rock types.

The granite has five distinct sets of fractures oriented at intersecting angles and the metamorphic Moine rocks also have their own fracture orientations. The presence of zones 50 metres wide of high fracture density, which may be continuous over distances of about a kilometre and extend to depths exceeding 200 metres, must have an effect on groundwater circulation.

The area consists of flat or gently rolling country between the 100 metres and 200 metres contours. Some researchers thought that the surface and groundwater systems were in hydraulic continuity (meaning that the geosphere and biosphere are linked by the movement of groundwater) (Kay and Bath, 1982); whereas others concluded that they were generally separate, except locally, where major fault and fracture zones would probably allow older groundwater from deep in the granite to reach the surface (Brereton and Hall, 1983).

The geochemical report (Kay and Bath, 1982) concluded that:

- groundwater in boreholes is a mixture of surface water and old groundwater.

- rapid downward movement of surface water to depths of over 160 metres can occur even in this low relief landscape.

- slow-moving, nearly horizontal flow systems probably link areas of recharge and discharge.

- faulting enhances the volume and rate of groundwater flow.

- the maximum age of the water is about 10,000 years.

- an active groundwater system such as exists at Altnabreac in fractured crystalline rocks can support conditions suitable for the transport of uranium away from a repository for times exceeding 10,000 years and to depths greater than 300 metres.

- boreholes drilled to only 300 metres provide insufficient data to assess the depth of an active flow system or how large the volumes of water involved might be.

In addition, the fracture analysis report (McEwen and Lintern, 1980) noted that in the light of the extensive near vertical fracturing and faulting in the area, it was unwise to assume that the number of closed fractures would increase with depth. So there is no guarantee that a deeper excavation at Altnabreac would encounter reduced groundwater flow.

However, because the fracture zones are markedly anisotropic, with vertical fractures predominating, and their origin can be attributed to known causes, prediction of their occurrence over a wider area may be possible (McEwen and Lintern, 1980). In association with further geochemical studies, a clearer picture of regional groundwater flow could then emerge.

The Altnabreac investigation is a good illustration of the problems of 'site investigation'. Despite four years of work and the publication of about twenty reports on different aspects of the geology, many questions remain unanswered about the suitability of the rock for waste disposal.

Billingham

Category of site: Inland sedimentary basin (see Figure 1.2 for location).

In 1983 there was a good deal of enthusiasm for evaporite rocks as containers for radioactive waste. At that time the preferred site in the UK for the disposal of long-lived ILW was a disused anhydrite mine at Billingham in Cleveland, but eventually public opposition forced the government to drop the plan. In 1989 Billingham still lies within Nirex's 'areas of search on land' (Figure 9.2) so a brief description of it is appropriate.

The geology at Billingham is simple. The potential site is a disused anhydrite mine in a sequence of sedimentary rocks. If water passes through anhydrite, the mineral dissolves. So it seems reasonable to conclude that *before* it was mined, very little groundwater had flowed through it in the approximately 200 million years since the deposit formed.

The anhydrite forms a layer about six metres thick within a varied sequence of evaporite minerals, overlain by 150–250 metres of calcite-rich mudrocks (often called marls), shales and sand-stones. The mine excavations have left a series of large caverns interrupted by massive supporting pillars of anhydrite; the excavated volume is about 11 million cubic metres (Openshaw *et al*, 1989).

Ginniff (1985) has estimated a groundwater flow into the mine of only about 13 litres per minute. By simple calculation, that is getting on for 70 million litres in the first hundred years after closure of a repository constructed there. It may be that, in the long-term, dissolution of the anhydrite is a possibility. Dissolution of anhydrite has certainly occurred not far away in South Durham, leaving a thin clay residue so that the overlying rocks have collapsed.

Other aspects of evaporites as hosts for radioactive waste are dealt with in the discussion of HLW disposal in Appendix 2 (*q.v.*) but some specific circumstances at Billingham could be significant. Immediately above the anhydrite is the Sherwood Sandstone aquifer; so the direction of groundwater flow in the vicinity of the infilled mine would be critical, since vertical flow could, in theory, result in contamination of the aquifer. There is also an area nearby where salt mining has been done by pumping down water to dissolve the salt and extracting the resulting brine (salty liquid). The result is a series of brine cavities where the introduction of water has the potential to further alter the chemical and mechanical properties of the surrounding rock.

On the positive side, the mine provides geologically stable, alkaline conditions, with a possibility of some sorbtion in the overlying rocks.

Summary

Safety in a deep radioactive waste repository ultimately depends on geological containment, but geological criteria are only one facet of site selection.

Preliminary investigations at Altnabreac and Billingham, as well as Sellafield and Dounreay, have highlighted substantial geological problems and, above all, uncertainties related to containment. The geology and hydrogeology at the sites were poorly understood when the choice was made.

In some respects both sites selected for detailed investigation meet some of the general geological criteria for effective containment. For instance, both are in low-lying areas above thick, laterally extensive rock masses situated several hundred metres below the present ground surface, and are unlikely to be directly affected by severe earthquakes. However there is complex faulting in the Sellafield area and there may be faults on site at Dounreay. Nothing is known about the extent of fracturing or permeability of the repository host rock at either site, but in both cases the overlying sediments are known to have high fracture permeability and to offer little prospect of significant sorbtion of radionuclides. At Dounreay, the effect of nearby salt water on the rate of flow and the pathways of groundwater return to the biosphere is also unknown. There is no convincing evidence to support Nirex's claim that groundwater emerging from a repository at Sellafield would necessarily follow a long, slightly downward pathway out under the sea.

Our knowledge of many other features relevant to containment is uncertain. The character of the basement rocks, as well as their exact depth below the surface, was unknown when site choices were made. The hydrogeology of the sites was also poorly understood, although educated guesses had clearly been made on the basis of general principles.

It is difficult to avoid the conclusion that the choice was strongly influenced by the prior existence of major nuclear installations at the Sellafield and Dounreay sites. Although some of the geological criteria set out at the beginning of this Chapter are met by these sites, several criteria are either not met or had not been investigated at the time of the choice.

Much obviously remains to be done if either Sellafield or Dounreay is to be proved geologically suitable for a deep repository; the next Chapter reviews some of the principal methods likely to be used in actual investigations.

Chapter 10

Investigating a Site

Once a radioactive waste disposal site has been selected for detailed investigation, an accurate picture must be built up of how containment would be likely to operate in the short and long term. This picture can be built up through a variety of field and laboratory techniques. Some of the most common ones are outlined in this Chapter.

The Aims of Site Investigation

These include:

*   building up an accurate three-dimensional picture of the rock structures beneath and around the site.

*   understanding the rate and extent of groundwater circulation.

*   discovering pathways linking biosphere and geosphere.

*   finding out about the transport of radionuclides.

*   understanding the rock mechanics (how the rocks would behave under various kinds of stress, including excavation, raised temperature and gas build-up).

A site must become, in effect, a field laboratory, where detailed observations can be made and where theoretical and laboratory studies can be tested.

Boreholes

Boreholes and rock cores extracted from them can be used to

investigate buried rocks and rock structures, groundwater circulation and groundwater chemistry.

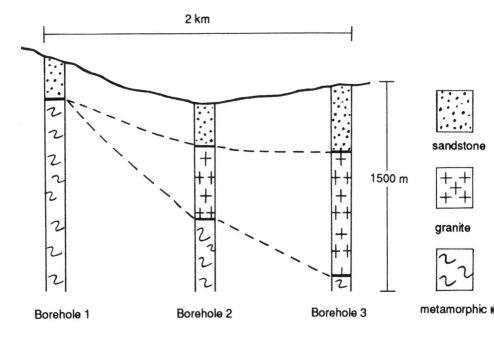

Figure 10.1 Correlation of rock formations between
boreholes. The granite does not appear in the left-most
borehole, and so the position of its margin is uncertain.
It is reasonable to assume that another borehole between the centre and right-hand borehole would cut the
same rocks seen in the boreholes.

A rock core a few centimetres in diameter and up to thousands of
metres in length can be extracted from a borehole to provide a long
thin vertical (or angled) sample of what lies beneath the ground
surface. If several boreholes are drilled, they can be correlated
(Figure 10.1) to provide an interpretation of the geology between
the boreholes.

Cores can provide a lot of very detailed information about the precise types of rock and their thicknesses and position relative to each other. The number of fractures per metre at different depths can be counted and they can be classified as open or closed. It is even possible to lower tiny television cameras down the borehole for observation of fissures and their orientation. The existence of permeable and impermeable strata can also be verified, and material is available for laboratory tests on chemistry, sorbtion and mechanical strength.

Boreholes at Dounreay and Sellafield, drilled to depths of up to 1,500 metres, form part of Nirex's site investigation programme. This is far deeper than the three to six hundred metres often quoted as a likely depth for a repository. But below 1,500 metres, groundwater flow is highly unlikely, so boreholes of up to 1,500 metres should provide information about regional flow paths and the extent of faulting and fracturing. However, cores are time-consuming and expensive to drill, so their number is always kept to a minimum.

Although cores can be very informative, their extraction does present some practical difficulties. Some sections of core will always be completely broken up or significantly altered by the very process of extraction, especially if there are soft or friable layers (such as shale) or a zone of intense fracturing. Moreover, in a borehole which is only 10 centimetres across, vertical (or near-vertical) fractures would only show up very occasionally if their average spacing was more than 10 centimetres. This can give a misleading view of the number of fractures present (Figure 4.5). That in turn may cause an underestimate of the amount of groundwater likely to flow through fractures to and from the surface. There is also the problem of interpolation — that is, making an informed judgement about what lies between two widely separated boreholes. What seems reasonable or likely is not always the case, so additional means of verifying and refining borehole information are needed.

Pairs or groups of boreholes can also be used to measure rates of groundwater flow and to determine the nature of the water table by means of pumping tests and flow meters. Tracers in the form of dyes or brines (salty water with a distinctive chemistry), or short-lived radionuclides, can be injected into boreholes and their dispersion and rate of movement measured.

The use of combinations of tracers, some of which are weakly sorbing and some of which are strongly sorbing, can provide information on the likely behaviour of migrating radionuclides. Of course, experimental techniques are rarely straightforward. The problem with this kind of study is that results may well be ambiguous: it may not be possible to tell which particular interaction or retardation mechanisms have produced the observed result (Chapman and McKinley, 1987).

Measurements of variations in water temperature and chemistry, as well as detection of 'wet' fissures, can also be made in boreholes. The significance of temperature variations is that they can indicate where the water has come from and how long it has been there — and thus contribute to studies of the residence time. Deep groundwater has a fairly constant temperature, gradually increasing with depth; surface water varies in temperature according to the season of the year, so contrasts can be detected.

Investigating water chemistry in the field also has its problems. Drill bits get extremely hot, unless the drilling face is flushed with compressed air and water and a variety of drilling fluids. This alters the water chemistry at depth, so that it may take months after drilling has ceased before natural conditions resume. Even then, bacterial contamination or the presence of solids from drilling fluids in fractures can cause problems of interpretation.

Samples of groundwater can be taken from deep in a borehole, but water chemistry may change if it is allowed to depressurise during sampling. For example if carbon dioxide gas escapes as the water reaches surface pressures (in the same sort of way that fizzy drinks fizz as a can or bottle is depressurised by opening it), the water will become much less acid, that is, its pH will rise. Such measurements could affect estimates of radionuclide solubility and mobility.

Geophysical Surveys

Geophysical techniques are used to help build up a picture of regional groundwater flow paths and to estimate where flow boundaries exist. The most commonly used techniques are seismic, gravity, magnetic and Very Low Frequency (VLF) surveys. VLF surveys are particularly useful for detecting faults in crystal-line rock (Chapman and McKinley, 1987).

Magnetic and gravity data obtained from airborne surveys provide information about rocks beneath the surface. The data can be presented as maps, a bit like contoured Ordnance Survey maps. Instead of height above sea level, the lines represent changes in the density and magnetism of the rocks. Different rock types have different combinations of density and magnetism, so the magnetic and gravity data can be used to predict the nature and extent of the rocks beneath the surface.

The technique of seismic surveys has been very highly developed by the petroleum exploration industry and much useful and accurate information can be gained to depths of a few kilometres. These surveys are conducted by generating seismic waves artifi-cially at the surface, using a very large hydraulic hammer, an air gun (often used in marine surveys), or a small explosive charge. These seismic waves have a tiny fraction of the energy of earth-quakes, but they are strong enough to travel down into the Earth's crust and to be reflected back from boundaries between contrasting layers of the rocks below. The time taken for the waves to travel down and return can then be used to measure the depth to the reflecting boundaries. In land surveys the vibrations to be recorded can be generated by machines mounted on large vehicles. Although the recording equipment and interpretation is highly sophisticated, generating the seismic waves simply means thumping the ground hard with a big, hydraulically-operated hammer. A survey of this type was done at Dounreay in December 1988 to provide information about where to site two very expensive boreholes 1,500 metres deep .

Computer programmes are now available which allow geologists to view seismic data in colour, in three dimensions, from selected angles and at selected depths. Seismic surveys can detect faults where the movement up or down the fault plane has been as little as 5 metres, but structures smaller than this cannot be detected.

As with most investigative techniques, however, interpretations are sometimes disputed. For instance, rock boundaries and seismic reflection boundaries do not necessarily coincide. Investigative science is rarely a case of applying a technique and then standing back and watching the results pop out with the reliability of sausages from a sausage machine.

Isotopic Tracers

To describe and predict pathways (or the absence of pathways) linking biosphere and geosphere, it is important to know where groundwater has come from and how long it has been there. For instance, if water in the area of a proposed waste repository was several thousand years old, and its chemistry indicated that no recent surface water was present, this would be a promising indicator for hydrogeological containment — provided that neither repository construction, natural events nor human intrusion altered the situation, of course, and providing that the finding applied to a sufficiently large zone of the geosphere.

Both stable and radio isotopes (Appendix 1) are useful tracers of the age and origins of water. Radio-isotopes useful in groundwater chemistry include carbon–14 which has a half-life of 5,600 years and tritium (hydrogen–3) with a half-life of about 12 years. Two other oxygen isotopes, oxygen–18 and deuterium (hydrogen–2 or heavy hydrogen) are also particularly useful since, like tritium, they can actually form part of the water molecule H_2O which consists of two hydrogen atoms bonded to one oxygen atom. So wherever water goes, so do these isotopic tracers.

Small amounts of tritium form naturally in the upper atmosphere and under normal conditions. The concentration in rain is less than 10 tritium units or TU (the concentration is one TU if there is one atom of hydrogen–3 to 18 million 'ordinary' hydrogen–1 atoms). Tritium, like carbon–14, is also formed by the explosion of thermonuclear weapons. Between 1952 and 1964, when atmospheric tests of these weapons took place, the tritium concentration of rain rose sharply to over 2000 TU in the northern hemisphere (Price, 1985).

The short half-life of tritium means that concentrations of over 5 TU in groundwater today indicate that there has been recharge from the surface since 1952. Such data contribute to estimates of surface water and groundwater mixing, so that rates and pathways of groundwater flow as well as connections between biosphere and geosphere can be modelled.

The longer half-life of carbon–14 means that it is useful for dating water up to 30,000 years in age. Indeed this is the method which was used to establish that much of the groundwater beneath the Sahara infiltrated thousands of years ago.

The ratios of deuterium (hydrogen–2) and oxygen–18 to the much more abundant hydrogen–1 and oxygen–16 are, in principle, constant in water at a constant temperature, but various physical processes such as evaporation, condensation and temperature change alter the ratios. Once the water is below ground level, no further change occurs until temperature-dependent rock/water reactions begin to operate. By measuring the ratios, the processes to which the water has been subjected can be deduced. The behaviour of these stable isotopes has been well researched; reliable conclusions can usually be reached about the source and even seasonal availability of infiltrating water,and the extent of mixing with older deep waters.

Thermal Infrared Linescan Surveys

In the right conditions, infrared radiation reflected from the ground can be photographically recorded from an aircraft and processed to display variations in temperature on the ground. A common use of this technique is to record wasteful heat loss from buildings, but it can also be used to help determine the source of water in streams and springs at the surface because there are well-known reasons for temperature contrasts. Groundwater temperature remains fairly constant throughout the year, while surface water reaches minimum and maximum temperatures in late winter and late summer respectively. So these times of year are best for distinguishing surface water from upwelling ground-water. An infrared survey is a way of investigating a large area very quickly by scanning it from an aircraft fitted with special sensors.

Despite numerous technical problems, it proved possible in the early 1980's to record differences in temperature in springs, lochs and rivers in the Altnabreac area of Caithness as part of the HLW disposal research programme (Brereton and Hall, 1983). Temperature anomalies were found to be due to the emergence of groundwater at the surface. Indeed it was estimated that a high proportion of the flow of the numerous streams and rivers in the area was provided by groundwater emerging in river beds and banks.

However, the researchers concluded, on the basis of stable and radio-isotope studies, that most of what they observed was shallow groundwater less than thirty years old, circulating locally through soils and the weathered granite in the top forty metres of the geosphere. They found no systematic relationship between the emergence of groundwater and previously mapped sets of north–south fracture zones where groundwater flow might have been expected to concentrate.

This particular work provides some useful insights into the nature of field research. Some discharge zones (where groundwater emerged at the surface) were 'difficult to explain satisfactorily' and were thus disregarded from the point of view of drawing general conclusions. Curiously, no groundwater discharge to the surface was detected in zones where the density of open fractures was mapped as quite high. Why was this? Because the linescan technique was imperfect? Because the assessment of hydraulic conductivity was at fault? Because inaccurate assumptions had been made about groundwater circulation? Or because a real effect had been detected? In the late 1980's thermal infrared linescan is still in the experimental stage as a technique for identifying zones of groundwater discharge, some of which could represent the boundaries of local or regional circulation patterns. Where boundaries of flow paths are under the sea, their existence remains a matter for speculation — and important speculation where a proposed repository site is coastal.

Excavations

When other data have been collected, trial excavations are likely to take place. Underground research laboratories (URLs) are seen by some countries as an integral part of the basic research needed before final decisions can be made about underground disposal and specific sites, though none exists in Britain. URLs can be used for a range of research purposes including:

- verifying predicted groundwater flow.

- investigating rock mechanics.

- measuring the effects of major excavation on groundwater flow.

- measuring retardation.

- testing gas migration.

- gathering additional data with which to refine computer models.

At present, URLs in salt, clay, granite, volcanic rocks and mixed sedimentary rocks exist in West Germany, the USA, Switzerland, Sweden, Japan, Finland, Belgium and Italy. Only Sweden has so far felt ready to establish an actual deep repository, and their decision reflects the fact that all nuclear power stations in the country will be closed down by the year 2000 and must be decommissioned.

An international research programme in which Britain has been involved is being conducted at the former Stripa mine in central Sweden. Geophysical methods have revealed strong channelling of groundwater flow in fractured hard rock. Observing such pathways is a step towards predicting their existence, nature, scale and orientation in zones of fractured rock beyond the narrow limits of direct observation.

One interesting conclusion of the Stripa research project has been that values of hydraulic conductivity derived from single borehole testing do not necessarily identify major water-bearing features. The implication is that simply identifying apparently open wet fractures does not necessarily provide a good lead as to where flow channels exist. Realistic research will be both more complex and more difficult to understand than many investigations to date.

Experimental Results

The principles of the research methods outlined above are clear, but in practice clear-cut results are not always achieved. Experimental methods vary — and so do results. Some experiments represent conditions in the geosphere better than others. Contamination of samples can occur, and it may take time and ingenuity to account reliably for unexpected values. Conclusions are likely to be drawn on the basis of a combination of field measurements and laboratory tests. But field measurements are beset by problems of measuring what has been severely disturbed by the process of investigation, while the choice of samples for laboratory tests can crucially affect results and conclusions.

It is also necessary to remember that the application of these investigative techniques to predicting the long-term isolation of radioactive waste from the biosphere is very new. It cannot be assumed that research based on water extraction from aquifers or exploration for metals and oil forms a reliable foundation for such a different application.

Any statement that geological containment of radioactive waste has been proved to work needs to be understood for what it is: an interpretation of many individual research projects, each with its own problems of interpretation. Results of research are often not clear-cut; conclusions about how satisfactory theories are, or exactly how processes are operating in the field, may be arrived at gradually, with sudden revelation rarely the order of the day.

The painstaking and sometimes confusing nature of scientific research is succinctly summarised in the following quotation from a report by the Royal Swedish Academy of Sciences (Beijer Report, 1987) on radioactive waste disposal, which notes that each research method has 'specific drawbacks. Laboratory experiments are short-term experiments with the rock and water not in their normal state or altered as a result of repository conditions. Field experiments do not usually define the flow paths and the geochemical conditions under which flow occurs. Moreover, unique solutions to the results obtained are not usually available.'

The report concludes that within 10 to 15 years it may be possible to reach an international consensus about important assumptions which have to be made in modelling waste containment, as well as agreement on how and when particular models can reliably be used to represent the real world.

All this is a long way from claiming, as was done in 1985 by Nirex's Deputy Director, that the geological barrier to radioactive waste migration is a known feature (Beale, 1985).

Summary

Site investigation involves a combination of field, theoretical and laboratory research. Techniques used include ground-based seismic and VLF surveys, airborne magnetic, gravity and thermal linescan surveys, boreholes, hydraulic testing, excavations and computer modelling.

In some cases, such as flow through fractured rock or sorbtion, fundamental research involving international co-operation is continuing. In other cases, such as determining groundwater and rock chemistry, the purpose of research is to obtain site-specific information through a combination of experimental and well-established techniques. The complexity of the data, the inaccessibility of most of the geosphere to direct observation, and the importance of making long-term predictions about safety, mean that computer models are a very important research tool. Chapter 11 briefly outlines what such models are and what they can and cannot achieve.

Chapter 11

Computer Models

A **computer model** is not something you can get your hands on in the same way that you can spin a globe which is a physical model (a small-scale reproduction) of the world. It is a computer programme (or programmes) which, when appropriate quantitative data (that is, measured or estimated values) are fed in, provides a good representation of actual processes.

A model can handle a number of variables. It can be validated — or invalidated — by comparing it with the results of experiments, and by seeing how closely it predicts the behaviour of the actual system being modelled. It can also be used to predict what will happen in situations which have not yet been, or can never be, the subject of experimental work. The long time-scale of safety studies for radioactive waste disposal, the sheer number of variables, and the impossibility of more than fragmentary direct observation of the geosphere, mean that there is a limit to what can be done by experimental work, so that an awareness of how and why computer models are constructed is helpful in understanding how decisions about the safety of deep disposal are made.

Laboratory experiments can be done on bits of rock perhaps a metre long and taking up to, say, a year. This is a tiny scale compared to the geosphere, with regional groundwater flow paths tens of kilometres long and radionuclides with half-lives of many thousands of years. So any application of experimental results to safety assessments for a repository must obviously be cautious. In addition, chemical and physical conditions for rock in a laboratory are far from natural, particularly with regard to groundwater chemistry, zones of higher permeability, changes in rock chemistry and changing pressures and temperatures.

With field experiments, transport distances as long as a hundred metres might be examined — but the same time constraints apply as in laboratory experiments. Experiments can't be kept running for ten years, never mind ten thousand. In addition, flow paths and water and rock chemistry in the field may be poorly understood compared to laboratory conditions. In these circumstances it is not surprising that a great deal of reliance is placed on developing computer models, which can, in principle, simulate conditions over hundreds or thousands of years, large distances and many different combinations of known variables.

Solving Problems with Models

A model of flow through fractured, crystalline rock would have to include, amongst other things, information about the orientation, frequency, length and width of the fractures. The information would be in the form of numbers, and mathematical formulae relating the numbers to each other in what was believed to be a realistic way. The numbers would be derived either from actual observations and experimental results or, if none were available, from best estimates based on a general theory about how flow would occur. In the second case the model would be much less likely to be accurate because the data could be wildly wrong. Models of sorbtion have run into just this problem because much of the available laboratory data is known to be unrepresentative of what actually goes on in the geosphere.

Models are quite often constructed in the knowledge that basic information is lacking, but there can be two kinds of justification for this. First, experimental work may be very expensive, very time-consuming, require new and difficult techniques, or be very intrusive if it demands the use of heavy machinery, blasting or large excavations; life is a lot quieter and cheaper in the computer room. Second, inadequate data in a computer model may be deliberately used in conjunction with experimental work, so that each can improve the quality of the other. The idea is that the formulae representing relationships between variables in the model can be refined as a result of experimental work, and the experimental work can be designed to test uncertainties in the model. As the model becomes more refined and more reliable it can be used to investigate problems when it is impractical to do so experimentally.

Predictive Models

Predictive models tell you what you would find if you could do the right kind of practical investigation or experiment, and what would happen if a particular set of circumstances occurred. An example would be a model which told you how far particular radionuclides would have migrated through a particular rock formation one thousand years from now in a coastal repository if the sea level rose five metres.

One of the problems in constructing good, predictive models relates to the number of variables involved. For instance, suppose flow through a sandstone is to be modelled and there are only two things which could affect flow: the permeability of the rock (which we shall assume is constant, although in fact it is never constant in nature) and the amount of percolating groundwater, which is known to be a simple proportion of rainfall. A model can then be constructed on the basis of one variable — rainfall, assuming that the permeability is constant. So in this example, when rainfall increases, flow increases proportionately. A few simple formulae will suffice to predict flow during periods of maximum, minimum and average rainfall, or for any given figure in between.

Suppose now, more realistically, that permeability was also

variable; the model, even with only two parameters, becomes much more complicated and prediction correspondingly more difficult. Permeability might vary with depth, perhaps in a combination of gradual increases and decreases, perhaps in discrete jumps between different strata. It may vary because the shapes and sizes of fissures and pores affect the flow of water. It might vary catastrophically in response to an earthquake, faulting, or gas build-up; it might vary locally in response to changes in water chemistry which initiated precipitation or dissolution of formerly stable minerals in pores or fissures. The data used in the programmes. and consequently the results, will depend crucially on what the researcher decides is significant.

A complete model would now have to account for, and predict, flow associated with a range of rainfalls for each state of permeability which has been envisaged and each possible combination. If it was to be used for risk assessment, it would also have to take into account the probability of certain combinations of circumstances occurring. Real models developed for research in radioactive waste disposal are of course much more complex. So the question is sometimes asked whether the models can be sufficiently reliable, given the degree of complexity and the use of sometimes poor data (RWMAC 9th Annual Report 1988; Lever, 1989).

Predictive models may even apparently work well for some time; then an observation is made which doesn't fit the pattern. Frequently workers assume that it is the observation or measurement which is aberrant, as indeed it may be. However, as every experimental scientist knows, there is a temptation to go on making measurements until 'suitable' results appear, that is the ones which fit the existing model!

So far we've only considered a model involving two variables. But of course many variables may be involved in the kind of models needed to predict long-term geological containment of radioactive waste. So the range of possible scenarios can quickly increase to calculations unmanageable except by powerful computers. One of the challenging features of multi-variable models is the need to predict which features become critical in different combinations of circumstances. This can be illustrated by means of a simple analogy.

Suppose you wanted to predict when people who usually love coffee will go off it. The variables might be pregnancy, serious illness and hangovers. Clearly not everyone in each condition is revolted by coffee. But a throat infection (not in itself a critical factor) might be critical in putting some pregnant women off it; more research would be needed to discover the critical factor for others. Alternatively, it might be found that only a particular range of illnesses was related to coffee revulsion. Yet again, an additional genetic factor might be found to trigger off coffee revulsion in people with hangovers, but have no influence on pregnant women or people with illnesses.

To put this in a geological context, you might establish that minor earth tremors would not affect either local or regional flow significantly at a certain site. But what if tremors occurred in conjunction with climatic change which could have significant effects on hydrogeology? Would tiny tremors — in themselves insignificant — trigger a major change in groundwater flow, groundwater chemistry and radionuclide escape? This kind of prediction is particularly hard to make and particularly important.

Simplifying Assumptions

Computer models need to start with some simple principles which can be added to and refined as the programme itself, in conjuction with field and laboratory studies, makes more or better information available. For instance, studies of groundwater movement through apparently randomly-oriented fractures in granite or gneiss have produced one- and two-dimensional models. These are not an appropriate basis for arguing that a particular type of rock or geographical area would be good for waste containment; after all, our world is three-dimensional. It is impossible to choose a representative cross-section (a two-dimensional model) to model flow in fractured hard rock because there is no such thing as a representative cross-section in the system (Rae and Black, 1986). Time is a fourth dimension which must be taken into account. Clearly, translating geological systems into a form suitable for modelling is very much a matter of judgement rather than cut and dried procedures.

Another very common simplifying assumption used in modelling is that a particular variable is uniform in space or time whereas in a real system (the geosphere), it is *variability* rather than uniformity which is common. Modelling sorbtion poses particular problems because guesses (albeit educated ones) have to be made about processes which are poorly understood. And in order to derive values to feed into the computer programme, reliance must be placed on laboratory experiments which are known to be unrealistic (Chapter 6).

Many of the mathematical models of radionuclide migration in the geosphere currently being developed are based largely, or entirely, on laboratory studies. But the real geological environment can be so different that their applicability may be questionable. For instance, whether fractures are open or closed will depend partly on the stresses acting on rocks in the field. Clearly this cannot be replicated in the laboratory measurements on which other parameters of the model are based. Neither can flow patterns over metres and kilometres and realistic water chemistry be observed in rock samples in a laboratory.

Averaging

There is an argument that computer models produce average values which fit well with the time-scale of geological containment, since the rate of groundwater movement in and around repositories would be so slow (on a time-scale of years and decades) that only averaged values would be meaningful anyway. Local or short-term variations are evened out over a long period. This means that the time and physical scale on which observations are made — and on which models are based — is vital. Look too closely and you won't see the wood for the trees.

In experimental science, atypical values — the very opposite of averages — are common and may simply be set aside as 'unrepresentative'. Nevertheless they exist and there could be circumstances in which they are significant. The problem is to know when. Each potential repository site will have special features which have to be researched and built into a modified, site-specific model if they are judged significant.

Probabilistic models

In probabilistic modelling, the values used in the computer model range from those with the highest statistical probability of being correct to those with a lower chance of being right. The large range of predictions thus generated allows the significance of different combinations of values to be explored. To some extent, this allows us to approach the problem by trying out the worst possible set of factors (eg. highest water flow, lowest sorption), and then considering the outcome. However, this 'What if...?' approach is only helpful if the model is reasonably accurate.

Garbage In — Garbage Out?

Computers are (so far) relentlessly logical. You feed them information and they process it according to set instructions. It follows that poor information and poor instructions produce poor models and inaccurate answers; this is the garbage in, garbage out syndrome. This is not to deny that complex models have proved successful; just that they need extensive testing and excellent input data before they can be taken as reliable. When the variables must include, for instance, long-term climatic change which itself is difficult to predict, the odds against the model being adequate increase.

In their 1988 report, the Parliamentary Committee on Radioactive Waste Management (RWMAC) advised:

'Future policies must avoid excessive demands upon modelling resources or the development of models beyond the level and range of available data.'

This statement, together with the establishment of a RWMAC sub-group to look at the issue, seems to imply that 'excessive demands' and unreasonable development of models of repository behaviour have indeed occurred, at least in the eyes of the parliamentary advisory committee.

Summary

Research into geological containment of radioactive waste must rely heavily on computer-based predictive models — not only because we must be sure containment would operate effectively over very much longer time spans than the life of a mere experimental scientist, but also because most of the geological environment is inaccessible to direct observation.

It is a commonplace in geology that the further back you go in time through the geological record, the less fine detail can, in general, be distinguished. By analogy, it seems logical to propose that the more long-term a prediction is, the less reliance can be placed on fine detail. Field workers know that if you are not looking for something you tend not to see it. The problem with modelling long-term containment is that researchers may not see, or accord significance to, some variables until a much later stage.

This chapter completes our review of geological containment of radioactive waste. Geological containment of LLW and ILW is UK policy and Nirex has the task of putting the policy and the waste in place. The question remains: 'Is this the way forward?'

Chapter 12

The Way Forward?

The question behind all the information in this book is, 'Would geological containment of radioactive waste actually work?' The answer, as should now be clear, is not straightforward, even if we treat the issue as a purely geological one. But perhaps we can get nearer to an answer by breaking down the original question into three questions:

1.   What precisely do we mean by 'Will it work?'

2.   Do we have enough knowledge of the behaviour of radionuclides in the geosphere to undertake the task of creating a single, permanent, national deep repository for radioactive wastes?

3.   How useful is it to consider geological criteria in isolation?

Each of these questions is addressed in turn below. There are clearly many additional valid questions about waste disposal but they fall outwith the scope of this book.

What do we mean by 'Will it Work?'

Suppose a young person without much money buys an old car which has been done up just enough to get an MoT roadworthiness certificate. It loses power a bit on the hills for some unexplained reason, the dashboard light only operates intermittently, the door sills are rusting and the suspension is uncomfortably soft. But does it work? Yes, no problem! It lives up to the driver's expectations (if not fantasies) and does more or less what is required of it.

However, no rally driver would risk competing in such a vehicle. It wouldn't be up to the job; it simply wouldn't work.

The point is that whether we think something works successfully depends on our definition of the job to be done. The two examples above perhaps represent the extreme ends of a spectrum. Most definitions of tasks include risk assessments and therefore compromises, so fall somewhere in between the extremes.

The principles on which the 'job description' for radioactive waste disposal is based are clearly set out in a variety of UK and European Community Acts and Directives which say it must work according to the following specifications:

'...the risk or probability of fatal cancer, to any member of the public, from any movement of radioactivity from the facility, is not greater than one in a million in any one year.'

This is certainly a low risk, though according to the UKAEA Information Office about 12 times greater than the risk of being struck by lightning! However, a problem with statements of this kind is that there are many uncertainties about the exact relationship between levels of radioactivity, radiation doses and the induction of cancer. So even if researchers were satisfied that radiation leakages in the long term could be accurately predicted, it would be hard to be confident about the level of risk. Additional risk associated with the transport of waste and repository operation is not included. Nevertheless, the statement provides guidance as to what level of risk is officially acceptable.

A second principle is that:

'There must be adequate provision for environmental monitoring...'

This sounds reassuring but 'adequate' is a difficult word to pin down. There is no absolute, scientific scale for measuring 'adequate', and it is a matter of judgement when enough is enough. What is more than adequate transport for the school leaver with a first car is woefully inadequate for the rally driver. Groups of interested people often have deep disagreements about the interpretation of the word 'adequate'.

Imagine, for instance, a coastal repository where 'adequate' monitoring suggested that the facility was operating well within the levels of acceptable risk. Would it still be adequate if high levels of radiation were eventually found in marine ecosystems because of unmonitored and unexpected leakages to the sea bed?

If we ask the question 'Will geological containment of radioactive waste work?' we must first define what we mean by 'adequate containment'. Two extreme views of adequacy might be:

- 100% containment guaranteed to operate for the many millions of years required for the decay of the radionuclides with the longest half-lives.

- Minimal compliance with regulations which are loosely interpreted in the manner most favourable to current political and commercial interests.

In the first case, the demands are so stringent as to be impossible to fulfill. Zero risk does not exist, but of course this does not prevent people from making such demands. The second proposal is clearly inadequate since it treats public opinion, safety and scientific work with contempt. One of the points of spelling out these two extreme views is that it is common to hear opponents and proponents of deep disposal arguing their case as if such extreme positions were the norm. Such a strategy is a barrier to a common understanding of what is meant by 'adequate working' of a deep repository, and it is only on the basis of this understanding that real discussion can begin.

The following anecdote illustrates the need for policy makers and participants in work on deep disposal to be honest about what they mean by phrases such as 'ensuring isolation from the biosphere' and 'geological containment will work'.

At the press conference called in March 1989 to announce the two sites in the UK (Dounreay and Sellafield) chosen for detailed investigation, the Managing Director of Nirex was asked by a journalist 'Can you assure us that there will be no leaks into the land or sea?' The journalist's assumption, and perhaps the common public assumption, was clearly that a repository that 'worked' ensured 100% containment. We don't know for how many tens, hundreds or thousands of years he thought this mattered.

The Managing Director's answer to the journalist's request for confirmation that there would be 'no leaks' completely obscured Nirex's definition of 'adequate containment', which could probably not be summed up in a couple of sentences. In reply to his question, the journalist was told how well-constructed steel packaging and thick cement would surround the wastes. The journalist clearly found this reply satisfactory and reassuring. Perhaps the view of Nirex is that public confidence in deep disposal would be shaken if it were widely admitted that *some* migration of radionuclides away from a repository is inevitable and that figures for radiation doses to individuals in the future are merely intelligent guesses based on preliminary information. So the journalist — and by extension the newspaper-reading, television-watching public — was implicitly encouraged in his erroneous definition of containment and safety.

Such assumptions are actively encouraged by Nirex. For instance, the statements 'there is no doubt that an underground disposal centre can be safely constructed' and 'natural geological features provide effective containment of radioactivity' are both from 'Going Forward, 1989'. However in more technical publications, such as the detailed safety report published by Nirex at the same time, numerous uncertainties are documented.

In between the extreme definitions of adequate containment discussed above is a whole spectrum of possible definitions, some of which are nearer to one extreme than the other. One intermediate definition of 'adequate containment' might be 'conclusively proven to cause less risk to the public than current methods of storage.' Another might be 'to the best of our belief, which is based on an expensive and extensive international research programme, highly unlikely to cause any problems up to the middle of the next century at least'.

So the question, 'Will geological containment work?' can only be sensibly answered if the questioner defines 'adequate working' which involves a definition of acceptable risk and is only indirectly concerned with geology. The questioner also has the right to know exactly what the political and practical definition of 'adequate working' of a repository is. The official answer is along the following lines:

'...understanding the scientific processes involved will enable predictions to be made about...safety...over a timescale of tens of thousands of years, beyond the next Ice Age. ... Deep burial of waste will ensure that the effects of disruption (by earthquakes, climatic change etc) do not breach the safety standards.' (Nirex: *The Way Forward* , p. 13).

'By choosing a geological formation in which water moves extremely slowly and in which radioactive species are readily absorbed and thus retained, it is possible to ensure that no significant levels of radioactivity enter the food chain.' (*The Management of Radioactive Wastes*, UKAEA Information Services Branch, 1987.)

'We are doing research to prove that deep disposal is safe.' (Mr. P. T. McInerney, Managing Director of Nirex, February 1988)

The import of these three statements might be summed up in the following way: we are sure that when we have learned enough about what we know only imperfectly at the moment, we will be able to justify our claim that deep disposal will meet safety requirements and prevent significant contamination of the biosphere. It is not difficult to understand why Nirex should prefer to make a different kind of statement at a press conference.

An alternative point of view is that it is dangerous to pre-empt the results of research, which might after all be negative or inconclusive. And if you know what research results you want, there is a tendency to arrange to find them.

There are plenty of signals around which should ring warning bells for those who are determined to claim that geological containment is the solution — and the only solution. For example, there are clear national differences, even between European nations, as to what constitutes 'safe disposal' although there is wide agreement that mined, geological repositories could, in theory, provide an option for radioactive waste disposal.

The reasons for such differences are not purely technical, but arise partly because of the gap between theoretical and experimental studies and actual sites. The nub of the problem is evident in an extract from an International Atomic Energy Authority paper on site selection factors (Beijer Report, 1987):

'The extreme complexity of many geological environments and of the rock features that govern the presence and circulation of groundwater does not make it feasible to derive strict criteria for the selection of a site for a radioactive waste repository in a geological formation. Each potential repository location must be evaluated according to its own unique geological and hydrogeological setting.'

In this context, the question 'Will it work?' becomes 'Will it work in this particular place?'; and this takes us to the question of whether enough reliable geological research has been done.

Geological Research

One way to start assessing whether enough is known is to see what the researchers themselves have to say and to set this alongside statements intended for the general public. The following quotations are from a mixture of research and review papers written since 1985, or from recent information booklets produced by the nuclear industry and in particular UK Nirex Ltd .

In December 1985, Harold Beale, the Deputy Head of Nirex, stated during a television interview that 'the geological barrier is a known quantity.' (Waste Not, Want Not, Channel 4 TV, 5th December, 1985). However, early in 1986, referring to the long-term geological disposal of waste, the First Report of the House of Commons Environment Committee, entitled *Radioactive Waste,* commented in unfavourable terms on 'the UK's backwardness in research and development'

The three volume Beijer Report on Radioactive Waste Disposal, produced in 1986 and 1987 by the Swedish Academy of Sciences, highlights in the following two quotations, both the beginnings of a consensus view and the problems of predicting the future with a high degreee of confidence.

'There appears to be an emerging technical consensus over the types of risks involved, the relative magnitude of potential consequences and likelihood of occurrence, and appropriate management responses (eg. multiple-barrier containment) for reducing the risks.'

'Among the intrinsic difficulties in risk assessment of long-term radioactive waste management, it is apparent that the limited ability to anticipate human actions even for the relatively near term (50–100 years) represents a continuing significant restraint. Our limited ability is shown by the often erroneous assumptions underlying five year economic plans or the loss of knowledge or institutional control at some radioactive waste sites over the past 25 years.'

There are also contradictory views about the extensive use of computer models in research related to repositories.

'The use of Probabilistic Safety Assessment in radioactive waste repository assessment has gained wide acceptance internationally and computer programmes for this purpose are in use or under development in several countries.' (Saunders, 1988).

'At the moment models outstrip the data and it is probably true that there are more models than sites modelled.' (Rae and Black, 1986).

Straightforward statements expressing full confidence in deep disposal of radioactive waste are also made.

'there is a recognised need...to establish permanent safe disposal facilities which will remove from future generations any burden of management of current accumulations and future arisings of such waste. The provision of a facility deep underground will do this.' (Nirex: *The Way Forward*, 1987, p. 5).

'FACT — The right rocks can hold it [radioactivity] in place for millions of years.' (Nirex, *Safe for All Time*).

'So the way in which the nuclear industry is proposing to dispose of....nuclear wastes is, in my judgement, safe and ought to be acceptable.' (Lord Marshall, Chairman, CEGB, *Your Radioactive Garden*, 1988).

These statements are judgements or interpretations of research work so it is worth going back one step and looking at what the researchers themselves say. There follows a small selection of examples which can be contrasted with public information statements by the nuclear industry.

'The magnitude of the effect of faulting on radionuclide migration is unknown.' (Black *et al*, 1987).

'We cannot interpret hydraulic tests in fractured rocks out to long distances.' (Chapman *et al*, 1987).

'At present we still lack a useful database on deep mudrock [fluid flow] properties which inevitably results in a circumspect approach to site selection.' (Chapman *et al*, 1987).

Nirex is undertaking 'a research programme into radionuclide transport from the near-surface geosphere into the soil zone and hence into biosphere receptors... This work has only recently begun or is still under consideration, and no results are as yet available.' (*The Nuclear Engineer*, vol. 29, No. 2, p. 56, March/April, 1988).

'Current levels of research are inadequate.' (Professor John Knill, chairman of the government's Radioactive Waste Management Advisory Committee, *Scotsman*, 22nd February 1989).

'The necessary testing, technological development and experimental work could not be carried out as a large-scale dry-run (i.e. research) exercise [that is, a trial excavation or large underground laboratory] simply because of the expense and the disruption that would be caused.' (Chapman *et al*, 1987).

'The study highlighted the difficulties of predicting the stability of stagnant groundwater zones resulting from small topographic features.' (Chapman *et al*, 1987).

'Drilling and excavation for the production of waste burial vaults will inevitably introduce...micro-organisms to deep repository environments, and the wide variety of organisms demonstrated in this study are capable of causing severe perturbations in the chemistry of an engineered barrier or groundwater system.' (Christophi *et al*, 1983)

'Many examples of gross alteration of groundwater chemistry by micro-organisms are known' (West et al., 1984).

'A typical water flow rate in deep low-permeability rocks is a few millimetres a year.' (Saunders, 1988).

'Fractured rocks can have exceptionally high hydraulic conductivities in fracture zones.' (Erikkson, 1985).

'This synthesis of geological, hydrogeological and geophysical approaches aimed at identifying the hydrogeological significance of faults has illustrated that there are a large number of unknown factors...which will have implications for radionuclide migration studies...' (Black *et al*, 1987).

'Field tests (for sorbtion) are expensive and notoriously difficult to perform and interpret...available data are insufficient to be used with confidence in the prediction of radionuclide migration at specific sites.' (Bradbury and Jeffries, 1985).

'The problem is that sorbtion is not well understood and is difficult to measure in a manner which relates to the real situation.' (D. George (UK Nirex Ltd.) and P. W Tasker (UKAEA Harwell Laboratory) in *Nuclear Engineer* April, 1988, p. 55).

'A typical result (of sorbtion) is that the concentration of radionuclides in the slow moving groundwater is only about a thousandth of the concentration in the radioactive waste packages themselves.' (Saunders, 1988).

'Sorbtion has been much studied in many national programmes. However, there has been a substantial variation in estimates of sorbtion data and considerable ambiguity in the interpretation of experiments.' (Lever, 1989).

'There are 7 radionuclides that do not adsorb readily to any material and/or have very long half lives; they will escape eventually from any containment system, including land-based repositories. They are technetium–99, carbon–14, iodine–129, neptunium–237, selenium–79, uranium–233 and palladium–107.' (Beijer Report, 1987).

'A substantial increase in repository pressure [from gas build-up] is not expected with fractured, hard rock.' (Presentation of the Nirex Disposal Safety Research Programme, 1988).

'In a typical deep repository, the volume of hydrogen produced each year would at most equal the volume of the waste itself... This is about a hundredth of the rate of gas production in a typical landfill site for domestic refuse.' (Nirex Research and Safety Assessment, 1988).

'The nature and quantities of gases likely to be produced...in repositories for low and intermediate level wastes are examined in this preliminary study. Many simplifying assumptions are made where published or experimental data is unavailable.' (Biddle *et al* 1987).

'Because there is virtually no experimental data on gas flow [through water-saturated, low permeability rock] modelling studies have to be based on assumed physical behaviour and parameters for gas migration, albeit that these may be constructed from knowledge of other situations.' (Rees and Rodwell, 1988)

A list of quotations of this kind could be as long as an argument. However, it is clear that there is one line of argument which more or less goes 'We don't know enough to predict confidently that radionuclides will be successfully retained in a deep waste repository.' On the other hand, managers and public relations staff for the nuclear industry through whom information to government and the public is filtered, make confident, reassuring statements. They quote typical research values to confirm the viability of geological waste containment and outline research programmes which will provide any necessary information which is lacking at present. They also express confidence that as yet unknown results of research will confirm their belief that plans for a mined, underground radioactive waste repository should go ahead.

These generalisations about the list of quotations above are echoed in a comment in the November 1987 Report issued by the Beijer Institute, which states 'we have found good agreement in general among the scientists of the various countries (France, Switzerland, West Germany, USA, UK and Sweden) on technical matters, [but] we have often found divergent responses to these questions by governments and other political groups.'

In the light of this sort of evidence, and with knowledge of the complexity of the issue, it is not easy to have confidence that the theory of geological containment of radioactive waste is well enough developed to form a firm basis for national policy. For instance, reassurances that sorbtion will prevent the passage of the great majority of radioactive substances in groundwater cannot be reconciled with other statements which stress lack of reliable experimental evidence. Reassurances that geological containment will provide permanent, safe disposal cannot be soundly based when research into gas overpressurisation, channelled flow and some aspects of radionuclide chemistry are in their infancy.

'National policy' of course involves political, economic and social issues, and there have already been hints that it is difficult to talk of geological criteria in isolation. This takes us to the third question that we posed at the beginning of this chapter.

Can geological criteria be considered in isolation?

On the basis of the discussion above, the answer is clearly no; research and the uses to which it is put are not the same thing. Moreover, while researchers may suffer from the 'the more you know, the more there is to find out' syndrome, people with an overview may see different perspectives.

Just as scientists have a vested interest in making the case for more research, so managers have a vested interest in selling a viable product or idea to the public and making systems work. Nirex certainly considers its work of site investigation for a deep repository as a commercial proposition and restricts access to research findings on the grounds that they are 'commercially valuable' (*pers. comm.*, Nirex Information Office, 1989).

Research does not take place in a social vacuum and is subject to a variety of pressures. Scientists, like managers and policy makers, are only human, and the quick fix of a problem by sudden discovery of a solution is intellectually and emotionally seductive. Scientists are no more nor less immune to human frailty and human error than anyone else, nor do they have a monopoly of common sense; but at least they have a healthy tradition of challenging established ideas.

In a very down-to-earth way too, the geological solution to radioactive waste disposal cannot realistically be considered in isolation. The engineering of very large, underground caverns would materially affect the hydrogeology, in predictable ways over about a decade and possibly in unpredictable ways over a longer time span. The building of a huge repository would also have an effect on rock stresses. In addition, the interaction of the site engineering and the geological environment would be important, particularly for hydrochemistry and gas migration.

Then there is the problem of small changes in complex systems having large consequences. Think, for instance, of a golfer who must hit a long drive down a narrow fairway. A tiny deviation of perhaps 2° to right or left will land the ball in tall trees or bushes and completely alter both the next few shots and the final outcome of the game. And the longer the drive, the further into the rough it will go.

Now suppose the narrow fairway represents a confident prediction of the fate of radionuclides in a repository and the length of the golf course the time during which containment must operate. A small deviation from predicted events could have substantial consequences, taking the radionuclides, like the golf ball, along unforeseen paths. Such consequences are familiar to other scientists such as ecologists and weather forecasters who know that in very complex systems, small events can have knock-on effects which lead to large, unpredictable changes.

And that, of course, is why neither ecology nor weather forecasting pretend to be exact sciences. Is the science of geological containment of radioactive waste any different?

Appendix 1

Atoms and Molecules

All matter is made up of simple chemical substances called **elements**, of which 92 occur naturally. A further dozen or so have been produced artificially. The smallest portion of any element is called an **atom.** More than 99.9% of the mass of an atom is concentrated in a very small **nucleus** (one nucleus, two or more nuclei) which is positively charged. The atom is electrically neutral; the positive charge of the nucleus is exactly balanced by **electrons**, negatively charged particles which can be visualised as orbiting the nucleus. The diameter of the atom is about 50,000 times the diameter of the nucleus. Most of the space taken up by the atom is completely empty — if the nucleus had the diameter of a golf ball then the outermost electrons of the atom would be about three quarters of a mile away.

The Nucleus

The nucleus is very much smaller than the atom. It has an internal structure of its own, consisting of two kinds of particles: **protons**, which are positively charged and **neutrons**, which have no charge. Protons and neutrons have about the same mass, and this mass is about 2,000 times that of the electron — this is why nearly all the mass of the atom is concentrated in the nucleus. The crucial factor that distinguishes the atoms of one element from those of another is the number of protons in the nucleus. The number of protons in the nucleus is called the **atomic number**. The total number of protons *and* neutrons in the nucleus is called the **mass number.** The fifteen elements with atomic numbers 89–103 are known collectively as the **actinides**. Thorium, uranium, plutonium and americium are all actinides. A particular nucleus with a given number of protons and neutrons is referred to as a **nuclide**; there are about 1,700 known nuclides.

Isotopes

Each element can have atoms with several different kinds of nucleus, but for any particular element, all the nuclei have the same number of protons (ie. the same *atomic* number) but may have different numbers of neutrons (ie. different *mass* numbers). Different kinds of atoms of the same element are called **isotopes** of that element; isotopes have different mass numbers because they have different numbers of neutrons in their nuclei. Thus all atoms of oxygen have eight protons in the nucleus, and therefore oxygen has an atomic number of 8. The most abundant form (isotope) of oxygen has eight neutrons as well, and thus has a mass number of 16. This isotope of oxygen is therefore referred to as the oxygen–16 (sometimes written as ^{16}O for short). A much less common isotope of oxygen has only six neutrons in the nucleus, and is therefore referred to as oxygen–14.

Radioactivity

Most of the nuclei of elements which occur naturally are stable and retain the same structure indefinitely. However, the nuclei of some naturally occurring elements, and of most artificially produced elements, are unstable. Unstable nuclei are said to be **radioactive**. Unstable nuclei will seek a more stable structure. The change to a more stable structure is accompanied by the emission of one or more different kinds of particle. This process is called **radioactive decay**.

In the majority of radioactive decays, three types of emission from nuclei can occur: **alpha particles**, **beta particles**, and **gamma rays.**

Of the 1,700 or so known nuclides, about 1,400 are radioactive. We refer to these as **radionuclides**. Most radionuclides are made artificially, but a number occur naturally, including carbon-14, potassium-40, and isotopes of uranium, thorium, and radium. Isotopes of an element which are radioactive are sometimes called **radio-isotopes**.

Note that different radioactive isotopes of elements are often referred to as radionuclides, without making a distinction between nuclides (which are strictly kinds of nuclei) and atoms, which are nuclei with attached electrons.

Radioactive Decay and Half-life

A useful concept to express the rate of decay of a radionuclide is **half-life**, the time it takes for *half* the number of nuclei originally present to decay. The half-life of radionuclides varies enormously from one type of radionuclide to another — it can be anything between fractions of a second and millions of years.

Activity

The activity of a radionuclide is the number of nuclei decaying per second. Activity is measured in **becquerels** (symbol Bq). One becquerel is equal to just *one* decay per second.

Nuclear Reactions and Chemical Reactions

Nuclear reactions are distinguished from chemical reactions by the fact that nuclear reactions cause changes in the *nucleus* of the elements involved. Since elements are characterised by the number of protons in the nucleus, nuclear reactions can change one element into another by changing the number of protons. Similarly, an isotope of an element can be changed into another isotope of that element by a change in the number of neutrons in the nucleus. Many nuclear reactions change the numbers of both protons and neutrons in the nuclei involved.

In contrast, chemical reactions do *not* involve changes in the nuclei of the elements taking part in the reaction. Only the outer electrons are involved in chemical reactions. Hence a chemical reaction cannot alter a radioactive atom into a non-radioactive atom — only a nuclear reaction can do that. So even burning (which is actually a chemical reaction) does not destroy radioactivity. Furthermore, radioactive isotopes of an element behave just like any non-radioactive isotopes of that element. The rules of chemistry operate independently of any instability of the nucleus. So, for example, radioactive potassium–40 can as easily be incorporated in living things as non-radioactive potassium–39 (the more common isotope of potassium).

Nuclear Fission

There is one very important way in which some very heavy nuclei decay, and that is by **fission**. Some heavy nuclei undergo *spontaneous* fission. However, a more important kind of fission is that *induced* when the nucleus absorbs an additional neutron There are only three nuclides for which fission is a significant decay process – uranium-233, uranium-235, and plutonium-239. Uranium–235 occurs naturally — it makes up about 0.7% of natural uranium, but plutonium–239 is not found naturally and can only be produced by a nuclear reaction.

When the nucleus of uranium–235 absorbs a neutron, it splits into two roughly equal fragments, together with the emission of further neutrons. There are a variety of possibilities for the fission fragments; nearly all of these fission fragments are radioactive. Energy is released in the fission, mainly as motion energy of the fragments.

In uranium which contains a high proportion of the 235 isotope, the extra neutrons produced can cause fission of other uranium nuclei, and if this proceeds unchecked, an enormous release and very rapid of energy occurs — this formed the basis of the first atomic bomb. In *natural* uranium, the fast neutrons produced by the fission of uranium–235 are captured by uranium–238. However if the neutrons are slowed down, fission of uranium–235 can proceed in a controlled way, and there is not so much capture of neutrons by uranium–238. The heat produced can be used to generate electricity; this forms the basis of most nuclear power reactors.

Many artificial radionuclides are formed in the fuel of a nuclear reactor, both from fission of the uranium, and as a result of neutron capture by the nuclei of uranium and other elements.

Actinides formed in the reactor by neutron capture include uranium–239, neptunium–239, plutonium–239, plutonium–241, and americium–241. Fission products formed include strontium–90, iodine–131, and caesium–137.

After a while, therefore, uranium fuel in a nuclear power reactor will contain many other nuclides, including plutonium and various fission products. Extracting the plutonium and unused uranium from spent fuel rods is called **reprocessing**, and in Britain is carried out by British Nuclear Fuels at Sellafield (formerly Windscale) in Cumbria.

Types of Nuclear Reactor

In Britain there are three types of nuclear reactor at present in operation:

Magnox

> This is the oldest kind of reactor in Britain. These reactors are reaching the end of their operating lives, and one has already been taken out of service.
>
> Examples are Hunterston A, Calder Hall, Wylfa, Bradwell.
>
> The fuel consists of natural uranium encased in magnesium

alloy. The spent fuel is stored under water, and must be reprocessed within 2–3 years because of corrosion of the fuel casings.

Advanced Gas Cooled (AGR)

Examples are Torness, Hunterston B, Heysham.

Fuel is uranium dioxide in stainless steel cladding. The spent fuel is being stored under water at Sellafield, awaiting the completion of a new reprocessing plant at Sellafield (THORP). This should be ready in 1990. In addition, it is planned to construct a dry store for AGR fuel at Heysham.

Fast Breeder Reactor

The British prototype reactor is at Dounreay. During the latter half of 1989, the government indicated its intention to end funding for the fast breeder reactor research programme.

Fuel is uranium and plutonium (obtained from Magnox reactors). Spent fuel is reprocessed at Sellafield.

A fourth type of reactor — the pressurised water reactor (PWR) — is under construction at Sizewell in Suffolk. This uses uranium dioxide as fuel, in a zirconium alloy cladding. PWR fuel can be stored more or less indefinitely under water until such time as reprocessing or disposal is selected.

A list of the radionuclides expected to be present in a British LLW/ILW repository is shown below together with their half-lives (Table A.1, after Nirex Report No. 71, 1989, Table 2.3). Note that short-lived nuclides with half-lives of less than one year are omitted. All the half-lives in this table are quoted in years.

The Forsmark repository in Sweden which is, at the time of writing, the only deep repository in the world actively accepting waste, is designed to contain waste for only 500 years. The Swedes aim to exclude radionuclides with a half-life of over 30 years, reckoning that within 500 years, all radioactivity will have decayed to harmless levels.

Table A.1 Radionuclides expected in a UK LLW/ILW deep repository.

Nuclides		Half-life (in years)
H-3	(tritium)	12.3
C-14	(carbon)	5,730
Cl-36	(chlorine)	300,000
Ca-41	(calcium)	80,000
Co-60	(cobalt)	5.2
Ni-59	(nickel)	75,000
Ni-63		100
Se-79	(selenium)	65,000
Sr-90	(strontium)	28.1
Zr-93	(zirconium)	1,500,000
Nb-94	(niobium)	20,000
Tc-99	(technetium)	210,000
Pd-107	(palladium)	6,500,000
Sn-126	(tin)	100,000
I-129	(iodine)	15,700,000
Cs-135	(caesium)	2,300,000
Cs-137		30
Sm-151	(samarium)	90
Pb-210	(lead)	22.3

Nuclides		Half-life (in years)
Ra-226	(radium)	1,600
Ra-228		5.75
Ac-227	(actinium)	21.7
Th-228	(thorium)	1.9
Th-229		7,340
Th-230		77,000
Th-232		14,100,000,000
Pa-231	(protactinium)	32,800
U-233	(uranium)	162,000
U-234		245,000
U-235		710,000,000
U-236		23,400,000
U-238		4,500,000,000
Np-237	(neptunium)	2,140,000
Pu-238	(plutonium)	87.7
Pu-239		24,400
Pu-240		6,580
Pu-241		13.2
Pu-242		376,000
Am-241	(americium)	458
Am-242m		152
Am-243		7,370
Cm-244	(curium)	18.1

[Note: no nuclides such as radon, polonium, bismuth and krypton which have a half-life of less than one year are included.]

Repository gases incorporating some radioactive carbon and/or hydrogen (tritium, deuterium) would be likely to include carbon monoxide (CO), carbon dioxide (CO_2), hydrogen (H_2) and methane (CH_4).

Some of the nuclides listed would be present in very small quantities, others in greater amounts.

In view of the list of radionuclides expected to be present in a UK LLW/ILW deep repository, for how long must containment work? The answer depends on the half-lives.

Cobalt–60 has a half life of about 5 years, so after 10 half-lives, that is, about 50 years, its activity will be about one thousand times less than when it was first stored. By contrast, the very long lived nuclides such as thorium–232, uranium–238, neptunium–237 and iodine–129 will still be highly radioactive thousands of millions of years in the future.

About 60% of the radionuclides listed above have half-lives of more than a thousand years, and some half-lives are up to a thousand million years. So even thousands of years after a repository was sealed a substantial proportion of the original radioactivity would remain.

Appendix 2

High Level Wastes

The main difference between HLW and ILW/LLW as far as geological containment is concerned is that HLW gives off large amounts of heat, as a result of the radioactive decay processes taking place in the waste. This affects rocks both mechanically and chemically, and would influence hydrogeology. Finding an underground site for heat-generating HLW therefore poses additional problems.

The bulk of Britain's HLW, produced by reprocessing nuclear fuel, is currently held at Sellafield and Dounreay. The intention is to store it there while the radioactivity decreases, for fifty years prior to vitrification and deep burial. Nirex has not been given the power to deal with high level wastes but this situation may change.

Nirex and Submarine Reactors

Before the end of the century, the Ministry of Defence will have the problem of disposing of ten obsolete nuclear submarine reactors, classified as HLW. Hansard, the official record of proceedings in the House of Commons, noted on May 25th 1988 that the Department of Energy had announced that 'sea disposal continued to remain an option for large items from decommissioning'. This is despite the fact that sea dumping of nuclear waste would be in breach of the London Dumping Convention, which in 1983 organised a ten year moratorium on sea disposal, and to which Britain was a signatory. These 'large items' could include intact submarine reactors. But in March 1988, Nirex was aware that the MoD was also considering the option of 'piecemeal disposal of the [submarine] reactor machinery in a deep disposal site to be developed by Nirex' as well as 'sea disposal of the entire submarine and land burial of the intact reactor.' (Nirex Information Office, pers. comm.)

However, involvement by Nirex in 'the increasingly pressing problem of the disposal of decommissioned submarine reactor compartments' (the Dreadnought has been laid up since 1982) was rejected by the Parliamentary Advisory Committee on radio-active waste management (RWMAC, 1988). Their report stated: 'We support the view that dismantling the bulky compartments and cutting up to enable packaging and disposal in the Nirex deep facility should be discounted for reasons of high operator radia-tion dose. A choice will need to be made in the near future on the policy for disposal as several submarines will be decommissioned during the 1990's.'

The UKAEA at Dounreay, which is to be in charge of the site investigations at Dounreay for a national deep repository, has, however, submitted a bid to the Parliamentary Defence Commit-tee for decommissioning nuclear submarines (*Observer Scotland*, 13th August 1989).

Closing Down Nuclear Power Stations

The volume of bulky HLW to be disposed of sooner rather than later has also been increased by the Department of Energy's decision in 1989 that all nine of Britain's oldest nuclear power stations, the Magnox series, will be taken out of commission by 2002.

Research into HLW Disposal

Between 1982 and 1987 the Sea Bed Working Group of the Nuclear Energy Authority (NEA) conducted a research programme into disposal of heat-generating wastes on, or within, deep sea sediments on behalf of the Department of Energy (RWMAC, 1988). The category 'heat-generating wastes' includes some high activity ILW as well as all HLW. The research zone was to the west of Madeira and the Canary Islands, in an area of deep ocean floor called the Madeira Abyssal Plain.

The general conclusion of this research done on behalf of the Department of the Environment was that radiological consequences of disposal were likely to be extremely small and that deep ocean floor disposal offered 'a feasible and safe alternative to disposal on land.'

The Parliamentary Advisory Committee (RWMAC) took a different view, expressing 'serious doubts' about site identification and characterisation as well as the technology of drilling and closing sufficiently big holes in the sea bed to receive the waste without them subsequently acting as short routes to the surface for migrating radionuclides. Because of these doubts, the Committee concluded in 1988 that 'the best option for heat-generating waste disposal in the UK has not yet been established.'

In the 1960's and 1970's most research into radioactive waste disposal concerned HLW rather than LLW/ILW, and rocks which might respond to heat in predictable and helpful ways were investigated. Rock types considered in Britain and elsewhere included:

1. large bodies of unfractured crystalline rock.

2. thick salt deposits.

3. plastic clays and clay-rich rocks.

Unfractured crystalline rock

Granite solidifies from a magma at temperatures around 7–800°C and so can withstand a considerable temperature. Estimated temperatures in a deep HLW repository could reach 150°C after

100 years (Milnes, 1985). Like most rock, granite is a very poor heat conductor, so heating by HLW might remain quite localised. As a result, the temperature would build up rapidly, which causes its own problems. Even 'unfractured' rock will contain some groundwater, and water expands on heating, creating high pressures in the surrounding rock. In such circumstances new open fractures could appear, altering the predicted hydrogeology.

Heat can also affect the rock minerals themselves. Granite, for instance, is generally composed of three main minerals, quartz, feldspar and mica. If mica or feldspar began to expand under the influence of heat but quartz did not, a series of new cracks in the rock could appear. Since granitic rocks have a limited potential for sorbtion, radionuclide migration might then occur in groundwater. Sorbtion itself is also affected by rising temperatures and seems to decrease quite rapidly as temperatures get higher (Roxburgh, 1987).

Evaporites

For some time, thick evaporite deposits have been considered to have good potential for HLW disposal, and the Asse salt mine in the Federal Republic of Germany was used for LLW/ILW disposal from 1967-78. In the USA, three underground research laboratories (URLs) were established in salt formations in Kansas, Louisiana and New Mexico. The WIPP (Waste Isolation Pilot Plant) site in New Mexico, due to accept its first waste in October 1988, suspended activities amidst a flurry of embarrassing publicity when seepage of corrosive brine was discovered. The reasons why this is likely to have happened were known to geologists in advance and are explained below.

The interest in evaporites for HLW disposal arose in the first place for two reasons. There exist in various parts of the world, including north-eastern England and under the North Sea, thick deposits of halite (rock salt), and also calcium sulphate (anhydrite). Both these minerals are anhydrous, that is there is no water in the mineral structure, and they form 'dry' rock. (Minerals which *do* contain water are said to be hydrated.)

The second attractive feature of evaporites for HLW disposal is that under high temperatures, salt deforms plastically, recrystallising and sealing up cracks. So in theory, these rocks provide a waterless environment which would automatically seal in radionuclides as the repository heated up.

Research has shown that evaporite deposits also possess other characteristics which do not favour containment. Evaporite deposits may contain a dozen different minerals in thin beds occurring at frequent and unpredictable intervals. Minerals such as carnallite, polyhalite and kieserite, which are hydrated or highly unstable, can decompose at low temperatures to give out large quantities of water, mechanically disrupting the rock at the same time (Chapman and McKinley, 1987; Roxburgh, 1987).

Fluid inclusions, (water/gas-filled cavities contained within single mineral crystals) are a further source of water in evaporites. These widely-distributed fluid inclusions can migrate towards a heat source, (such as buried HLW) carrying with them a corrosive brine (Milnes, 1985; Chapman and McKinley, 1987). The extreme saltiness of any water that does exist in evaporite deposits will result in rapid disintegration of steel and concrete.

The mechanical response of evaporite rocks to heating is also not as simple as first thought. Where there are different minerals, cracks may form as they expand at different rates, and the opening and closing of joints may reduce the strength of the rock. In addition, gamma radiation itself hardens rock salt, making it more likely to fracture (Milnes, 1985).

Clays

Clays have been investigated for HLW disposal because of their impermeability and high potential for sorbtion, and have been most intensively studied at Mol in Belgium.

Although unfractured clays and clay-rich rocks are impermeable, they may contain a high proportion of water-filled pores. In addition, some clay minerals are hydrous and the 'swelling clays' (equally justifiably called 'shrinking clays') trap and hold extra water when it is available. So clays are not dry rocks. Because clay-rich rocks contain water but are impermeable, the water cannot escape easily. If it were heated or converted to steam by the presence of heat-generating waste, its volume would increase, resulting in abnormally high pressures building up round the heat source. The effect is accentuated by the fact that heating itself tends to reduce permeability (Milnes, 1985). Sufficiently high pressures will lead to fracturing and increased permeability.

Gamma radiation directly affects clay minerals as well as salt. When clay minerals are irradiated their structure can break down, thereby releasing water to circulate in the vicinity of the radiation source.

Appendix 3

Abbreviations

AERE	Atomic Energy Research Establishment of the UKAEA.
BGS	British Geological Survey.
BNFL	British Nuclear Fuels plc.
BUSC	basement under sedimentary cover.
DoE	Department of the Environment.
ENPU	Environmental Protection Unit of the IGS/BGS.
FPLU	Fluid Processes Research Group of the BGS.
HGW	heat-generating waste.
HLW	high level waste.
IAEA	International Atomic Energy Authority.
IGS	Institute of Geological Sciences (now the BGS).
ILW	intermediate level waste.
LLW	low level waste.
NEA	Nuclear Energy Authority, Harwell, Oxfordshire.
NERC	Natural Environment Research Council.
NSS	Nirex Safety Studies.
pers. comm.	personal communication.
RWMAC	House of Commons Radioactive Waste Management Advisory Committee.

SKB	Statens Karnbransle Namnd [Swedish National Board for Spent Nuclear Fuel].
TDS	total dissolved solids.
UKAEA	United Kingdom Atomic Energy Authority.
URL	Underground research laboratory.
VLF	very low frequency.
WIPP	Waste Isolation Pilot Plant (New Mexico, USA).

Glossary

acidity: see pH.

aftershock: a secondary earthquake (sometimes one of many) which follows the initial release of energy in an earthquake.

alkalinity: see pH.

anhydrite: $CaSO_4$—a calcium sulphate mineral with no water in its structure.

anisotropic: having different properties when measured in different directions.

aquifer: underground rock from which water can be extracted.

basalt: a type of volcanic rock formed when lava solidifies.

basement: [synonymous with crystalline basement] deeply buried metamorphic and/or igneous rock beneath younger sedimentary rock.

bedding plane: a surface which marks the beginning of a particular episode of deposition of a particular type of sedimentary rock.

biosphere: the life-bearing surface of the Earth including living creatures and the soils, water and atmosphere in which they live.

Borrowdale Volcanics: the local name for the complex series of metamorphosed volcanic rocks making up the central part of the English Lake District. These rocks underlie Sellafield at a depth of about 900 metres.

calcium carbonate: a common, easily dissolved mineral which is the main constituent of limestone and acts as a cement in some sandstones.

cement: minerals which hold the particles of sedimentary rocks together. Calcium carbonate, silica, clay minerals and iron oxides are common cements.

clay: a deposit of uncemented clay mineral particles.

clay mineral: the smallest grade of sedimentary particle.

computer model: a computer program which contains a mathematical representation of natural phenomena and their relations with each other. The program allows a variety of likely events and circumstances to be investigated (modelled).

conglomerate: a sedimentary rock formed of pebble to boulder-sized particles.

core: a continuous cylinder of rock, usually not over 10 centimetres in diameter, extracted in a sequence of short lengths from a borehole during drilling.

country rock: pre-existing rock into which a plutonic igneous rock has been intruded.

crystalline rock: a rock composed of interlocking crystals. A broad term for igneous and metamorphic rock.

diorite: a type of plutonic igneous rock.

dip: the angle which sedimentary bedding planes make with the horizontal, as in 'seaward-dipping sediments'.

drift: a name for recent surface sediments which have been deposited by water, wind or ice.

crust (of the Earth): the outermost shell of rock covering the Earth, averaging 35 kilometres in thickness, and varying from 5–90 kilometres.

evaporite: a rock consisting of crystals formed by evaporation of salty water.

fault: a fracture of the Earth's crust along which vertical and/or horizontal displacement has occurred.

flocculation: the clumping together of clay particles to form larger particles which can settle out from suspension.

fracture: a break in a rock which cuts across natural rock boundaries on any scale from a mineral crystal to a thick sequence of different rock types.

geochemistry: the chemistry of rocks.

geological containment of radioactive waste: the use of natural properties of the geosphere to isolate radioactive waste.

geomicrobiology: the study of micro-organisms which live in the geosphere.

geosphere: the Earth's crust below the biosphere.

gneiss: a metamorphic rock formed at very high temperatures and pressures and often characterised by alternating light and dark bands of different minerals.

granite: a plutonic igneous rock which forms dome or sheet-like bodies up to several kilometres across.

hard rock: a term often applied to crystalline rocks.

hydraulic anisotropy: the property some rocks have of transmitting fluids more easily in one direction than another.

hydraulic conductivity: a measure of the volume of fluid which will move through an area of rock one metre square in a specified time.

hydrogeology: the study of water in the geosphere.

hydrogeological containment of radioactive waste: the use of groundwater circulation patterns to isolate radionuclides within the geosphere.

igneous rock: rock which has solidified from magma.

ion: an atom or group of atoms that has lost or gained one or more electrons, leaving it with a positive or negative charge, respectively.

isotope: isotopes are atoms of the same element but with different mass numbers (ie. the same number of protons, but different numbers of neutrons).

joint: one of a set of closely or widely spaced rock fractures with the same orientation.

lava: magma erupted by a volcano on to the Earth's surface (also used to refer to the *rock* formed in this way when the magma solidifies).

limestone: any sedimentary rock consisting mainly of carbonates.

local flow: a groundwater circulation cell which is shallow and localised, and in which groundwater has a short residence time.

magma: molten fluid rising up from great depths below the Earth's surface; the source of igneous rocks.

metamorphic rock: rock which has had its minerals transformed into other minerals by the action of heat and pressure.

mineral: a naturally occurring inorganic solid with a definite chemical composition and a definite crystal structure.

mudrock: a sedimentary rock formed largely of clay minerals.

organic molecule: a molecule containing the element carbon.

permeability: a measure of a rock's capacity to allow the passage of fluids.

pH: the scale used to express the concentration of free hydrogen ions in a water solution. A pH of 7 is neutral; a pH of less than 7 is acid; a pH of greater than 7 is alkaline.

plutonic rock: igneous rock which has crystallised (solidified) from a magma several kilometres below the Earth's surface.

pore: cavity between the mineral grains of which a rock is composed.

porosity: the percentage of rock volume occupied by cavities (pores).

precipitate: to form mineral crystals from a saturated solution.

quartz: SiO_2 A mineral which forms the majority of fragments in sandstone, and is an important constituent of certain crystalline rocks such as granite. Quartz also occurs as a cement in some sedimentary rocks.

recharge: the replenishment of an aquifer by percolating groundwater.

regional flow: a groundwater circulation pattern extending vertically down to 1,000 metres or more and horizontally to tens of kilometres.

residence time: the average time spent by substances such as groundwater or radionuclides in the geosphere.

Richter scale: a scale from 1 to 10 on which the amount of energy releascd by earthquakes is measured.

rock: an aggregate of grains of several minerals, or occasionally of grains of only one mineral.

sandstone: a fragmented rock composed largely of grains of quartz cemented together.

schist: a metamorphic rock with most of its minerals (commonly including mica) aligned in one plane.

seal: a rock or geological structure which prevents the passage of fluids.

sediments: uncemented sedimentary particles at the Earth's surface; sometimes used as a synonym for sedimentary rocks.

sedimentary basin: an area of the Earth's crust which contains several kilometres' thickness of sedimentary rock.

sedimentary rock: rock composed of particles of pre-existing rock and other materials held together by natural cements.

seismic zone: an area of the Earth's crust in which there is historical evidence for the occurrence of earthquakes or where they are predicted for geological reasons.

seismology: the study of earthquakes.

shale: a sedimentary rock formed largely from clay minerals which differs from mudrock in having closely-spaced, well-developed bedding planes.

silt: sedimentary particles intermediate in size between clay and sand.

soft rock: a term usually applied to sedimentary rocks.

solubility: the ease with which a substance dissolves.

sorbtion: the transfer of dissolved or suspended radionuclides from moving groundwater to the rock with which it is in contact.

superficial deposits: sediments deposited relatively recently by rivers, glaciers and wind.

Synroc: a glass-like artificial rock designed to incorporate HLW in a form suitable for disposal.

till: sediment, such as boulder clay, deposited by moving ice.

unconformity: a geological boundary, sometimes marked by a weathered surface, which records the passage of time between the formation of one sequence of rocks and the overlying ones.

volcanic rock: igneous rock which forms from magma which is erupted on to the Earth's surface; explosive or gas-rich volcanism can produce ash which forms bedded rocks, while less violent eruption produces flowing lava which solidifies to form rocks such as basalt.

weathering: the physical and chemical breakdown of rocks at the Earth's surface.

Selected References

Beale H (1985). The meticulous five steps in the search for a site. *Plaintalk*, Nirex, May 1985.

Beijer Report [See SKN Report 17].

Berry JA, Bourke PJ, Green A and Littleboy AK (1987). Sorbtion of radionuclides on hard rocks. AERE R 12844, UKAEA.

Berry *et al* (1989). Sorbtion of Radionuclides on the London Clay. AERE R 12978, UKAEA.

Biddle P, McGahan D, Rees JH, and Rushbrook PE (1987). Gas Generation in Repositories. AERE R 12291, UKAEA.

Black JH, Alexander J, Jackson PD, Kimbell GS, and Lake RD (1987). The Role of Faults in the Hydrogeological Environment. FLPU 86–9, BGS/NERC.

Bradbury MH and Jeffries NL (1985). Review of Sorbtion Data for Site Assessment. AERE R 11881, UKAEA.

Brookins DG (1983). Migration and Retention of Elements at the Oklo Natural Reactor. *Environ. Geol.* 4, 201–208.

Brereton NR and Hall DH (1983). Groundwater Discharge Mapping at Altnabreac by Thermal Infra–red Linescan Surveying. FLPU 83–7, BGS/NERC.

Chapman NA, McEwen TJ and Beale H (1986). Geological Environments for Deep Disposal of Intermediate Level Wastes in the UK. In: *Siting, Design and Construction of Underground Repositories for Radioactive Wastes*, IAEA, Vienna.

Chapman, NA, Black JH, Bath AH, Hooker PJ and McEwen TJ (1987). Site Selection and Characterisation for Deep Radio-active Waste Repositories in Britain: Issues and Research

Trends into the 1990s. FPLU, BGS/NERC.

Chapman NA and McKinley IG (1987). *The Geological Disposal of Radioactive Waste*, John Wiley and Sons, Chichester.

Christophi N, West JM, Robbins JE and McKinley IG (1983). The Geomicrobiology of the Harwell and Altnabreac Boreholes. FLPU 83–4, IGS/NERC.

Cook AJ (1988). A desk study of surface diffusion and mass transport in clay. BGS Technical Report WE/88/34.

Cooper MJ (compiler) (1988). *Nirex Safety Assessment Research Programme Bibliography 1988*. NSS/G107, UKAEA.

Davies (1989). As pure as the driven snow. *New Scientist*, 8th April 1989.

Erikkson E (1985). *Principles and Applications of Hydrochemistry*. Chapman and Hall.

Evans CDR and Evans D (1982). Geological Formations on the UK Continental Shelf in Relation to the Disposal of Solid Radioactive Waste. ENPU 82–3, IGS/NERC.

George D and Tasker PW (1988). The Disposal R and D Programme of UK Nirex Ltd. In: *The Nuclear Engineer* 29,(2).

Gilling D, Jeffries and Lineham TR (1987). An Experimental Study of Solute Transport In Mudstones. NSS/R109, Nirex Radioactive Waste Disposal Safety Studies, UKAEA.

Ginniff ME (1985). The implementation of UK policy and strategy on Nuclear Waste Disposal. *Nuclear Energy* 24(2), 94–104.

Godfrey M (1989). Quoted in *The Scotsman*, 25th October 1989.

Herbert AW, Hodgkinson DP and Rae J (1985). A pictorial view of radionuclide Migration from a Deep Underground Repository for Cemented ILW. AERE M 3496, UKAEA.

Herbert AW, Hodgkinson DP, Lever DA, Rae J and Robinson PC (1986). Mathematical modelling of radionuclide migration in groundwater. *Quarterly Journal of Engineering Geology*, 19, 109–120.

Hooker PJ and Chapman NA (Eds) (1989)   UKNACG Second Annual Report DOE/RW/89.021

IAEA (1977) Site Selection Factors for Repositories of Solid High Level and Alpha-Bearing Wastes in Geological Formations. Vienna, Austria.

Ivanovich M, Longworth G, Wilkins MA, Hasler SE and Lloyd MJ (1988). Measurement of Effective KD Factors for the Long–Lived Uranium and Thorium Isotopes in Samples of London Clay (Bradwell) and Mudrock (Fulbeck). NSS/R117, UKAEA.

Kay RLF and Bath AH (1982). Groundwater Geochemical Studies at The Altnabreac Research Site. ENPU 82–12, IGS/NERC.

Krauskopf KB (1988). Topics in the Earth Sciences Vol 1. Radioactive Waste Disposal and Geology. Chapman and Hall.

Lever DA (1989). Radionuclide Transport by Groundwater Flow Through the Geosphere: Current Status, NSS/G105, UKAEA.

Lilwall RC (1976). Seismicity and Seismic Hazard in Britain, Seismological Bulletin No 4 IGS/NERC, HMSO, London.

Mather JD, Chapman NA, Black JH and Lintern BC (1982). The geological disposal of high–level radioactive waste — review of the Institute of Geological Sciences' research programme. *Nuclear Energy*, Vol 21, No 3, 167–173.

Milnes AG (1985). *Geology and Radwaste*. Academic Press.

McEwen TJ and Lintern BC (1980). Fracture Analysis of the Rocks of the Altnabreac Area. ENPU 80–8, IGS/NERC.

Nirex: see United Kingdom Nirex Limited.

Openshaw S, Carver S and Fernie J (1989). Britain's Nuclear Waste. Belhaven Press, London.

Pilkington NJ, Shadbolt PJ and Wilkins JD (1988). Experimental Measurements of the Solubilities of Selected Long–Lived Fission Products, Activation Products and Actinide Daughters under High pH Conditions. NSS/R116, UKAEA.

Price M (1985). *Introducing Groundwater.* George Allen and Unwin.

Pryce MHL (1986). Principles governing deep groundwater flow. *Phil. Trans. Royal Soc. Lond,* A 319.

RWMAC (1988). Radioactive Waste Management Advisory Committee, 8th Annual Report, 1988, HMSO, London.

Rae J and Black JH (1986). Modelling of migration of leached radionuclides by groundwater. *Phil. Trans. Royal Soc. Lond,* A 319, 97–108.

Robins NS (1980). The Geology of Some United Kingdom Nuclear Sites Related to the Disposal of Low and Medium Level Radioactive Wastes. ENPU 80–5, IGS/NERC.

Rees JH and Rodwell (1988). Gas Evolution and Migration in Repositories: Current Status. NSS/G104, UKAEA.

Roxburgh IS (1987). *The Geology of High Level Nuclear Waste Disposal.* Chapman and Hall.

Saunders PAH (1987). An Outline of Nirex's Research and Safety Assessment Programmes. NSS/G101, UKAEA.

Saunders PAH (1988). Research and Safety Assessment, Nirex Radioactive Waste Disposal Safety Studies. NSS/G100, UKAEA.

Sinclair A (1988). *The Strange Tales of Causeymire.* Spittal Action Centre, Caithness, Scotland.

SKN Report 17. Statens Karnbransle Namnd (National Board for Spent Nuclear Fuel):. *Technical and Socio–Political Issues in Radioactive Waste Disposal.* Volume 1: Safety, Siting and Interim Storage. Volume 1A: Safety, Siting and Interim Storage. Appendices: Countries and International Organisations. Volume 2: Subseabed Disposal. Parker FL, Kasperson RE, Andersson TL and Parker SA. Beijer Institute of the Royal Swedish Academy of Sciences, Stockholm 1986/7.

Sumner D (1988). *Radiation Risks: An Evaluation* (second edition). The Tarragon Press, Glasgow.

Turbitt T (1986). British Earthquakes. In: *The Edinburgh Geologist* No 19, Edinburgh Geological Society.

United Kingdom Nirex Limited (1988). Presentation of the Nirex Disposal Safety Research Programme, NSS/G108.

United Kingdom Nirex Limited (1989). Report No 71, Deep Repository Project, PERA/PSR.

West JM, Hooker PJ and McKinley IG (1984). Geochemical constraints on the microbial contamination of a hypothetical UK deep geological repository. FLPU 84–8, BGS.

Woo G and Muir Wood R (1986). North Sea Seismicity Summary Report. Offshore Technology Report OTH 86219, AERE, HMSO, London.

INDEX